THE GARDEN OF LARKSPURS

THE MACMILLAN COMPANY
NEW YORK · BOSTON · CHICAGO · DALLAS
ATLANTA · SAN FRANCISCO

MACMILLAN & CO., Limited
LONDON · BOMBAY · CALCUTTA
MELBOURNE

THE MACMILLAN COMPANY
OF CANADA, Limited ·
TORONTO

The Candle Larkspur, one of the popular ornamental perennials.
The old-fashioned blue race is in the center background.

The
Garden of Larkspurs
With Decorations

By

L. H. BAILEY

NEW YORK

THE MACMILLAN COMPANY

1939

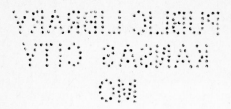

The Text

The Twenty-five Portraits

THE TWENTY-FIVE PORTRAITS

THE GARDEN OF LARKSPURS

The Garden of Larkspurs

WHEN MY SEED PACKETS are assembled it is noticeable that the annual species are called larkspurs and the perennial species delphiniums. This distinction may not hold in other languages, for I find the French equivalent of larkspur, *pied d'alouette* (larksfoot), applies to annuals and perennials alike on the packets. The regular delphinium growers in this country make distinction between the two groups, perhaps with a feeling of indifference for the annual species.

There is no warrant for this separation of names, as any person may determine by consulting the manuals of botany and dictionaries of the English language; nor would it be practicable to maintain the two names for plants differing merely in duration inasmuch as *Delphinium grandiflorum* (*chinense*) is often treated as an annual and others, as *D. Staphisagria*, are biennial. Delphiniums are larkspurs and larkspurs are delphiniums, and the subject is so understood in this writing.

If the reader wishes authority for the use of the word larkspur let him consult the great New Oxford Dictionary edited by Murray, where, in volume six, he will find it defined as "any plant of the genus delphinium; so called from the spur-shaped calyx." Historically, the case may not be as simple as this; thus Britten and Holland in their standard Dictionary of English Plant-Names in 1886 record different applications of the word larkspur and its variables in early time, one of them to the plant we now know as toad-flax; but the lexicon usage for current language is established.

Having now determined what we are to talk about in this our hopeful book, we may proceed at once to important matters; and the first impulse is to admire the sturdy rows of Rocket larkspurs in good view from my window as I write on this sweltry August day. Three months old they are; I sowed the seeds, more than a dozen named kinds, early in May when the promise of spring was at its height and the air was filled with fragrances and music; now they stand three to four feet tall, prim in their rows, glowing in spikes of white and blue and pink and purple, a pretty sight; the family cat likes to lie among them.

Close by them and in view from my table are large azure-blue clumps of the Garland larkspur, one of them Cliveden Beauty, and another the misnamed *Delphinium Barlowii*. The Candle larkspurs are now past their bloom, but one old clump stands in front of me six and one-half feet tall, holding aloft its upright seedful pods. Plants of Bouquet larkspurs, sown this spring, are in the planting, now coming into bloom. On my table in full flower is a complete plant of the singular *Delphinium cardiopetalum*, introducing the group of Forking larkspurs. Here, then, are all the five major groups of horticultural larkspurs, to keep my pen true to its purpose. Alongside them are several kinds of bellflower, about which we may learn in another year.

It has been a season of larkspurs, and I have lived again the joys I have had in growing them for more years than I can remember. This year I have seen them carefully in many gardens, and in commercial plantations where they are grown in tens of thousands. Here at my hand are books that account for them, photographs, and many hundreds of herbarium specimens of them that would only amuse the grower but which provide the only means of knowing what is what. Marian Wrench has again made me paintings, and Florence Mekeel has drawn the plates.

The blues of the larkspurs are a haunting memory of old homesteads, long sturdy rows by fences, of clumps persisting in grass. They belong with habitations of poor and rich alike, a common denominator of good will.

Yet not all the larkspurs are blue, not even in nature. There are reds and apricot colors, as in *Delphinium cardinale* and *D. nudicaule* (be careful to pronounce the final *e* of these and similar names, as if ending in short *y*). There is now good prospect of an important race of red larkspurs in the progeny of *D. Ruysii;* I shall welcome them but shall also keep the blues.

I fear that in the effort at novelty in color we are in danger of subjugating the old plain blue Candle larkspur; we have few enough good blue flowers. Nor am I much in sympathy with that attitude of delphinarians (to adopt Leonian's word) that restricts most of their activity to the Candle larkspurs with the constant effort to produce "breaks" and to isolate named varieties. The genus delphinium is yet scantily touched as a horticultural adventure nor do we know the prizes that might be earned by a wider spread of interest in native

LARKSPUR SEEDLINGS

kinds. Not more than perhaps a half dozen species have been much ameliorated for horticultural uses. I would keep all the good garden varieties we now have, and produce others, but I wonder what lies elsewhere and beyond. Possibly the present formal standard as to what constitutes a proper delphinium will not continue to be sufficient.

The historic literature of delphinium lies in the manuals that treat the flora of different regions, and if the reader is antiquarian he may go into the many herbals of centuries ago where the plants are explained under terms and appellations strange to us in these late days. All these works are not horticultural, as we now like to define that word. In recent time we have the three books published in England, by A. J. Macself, J. F. Leeming and George A. Phillips, and in North America the book, How to Grow Delphiniums, 1935, by Leon H. Leonian, Editor of the American Delphinium Society. Many other books include chapters or paragraphs on Delphinium. A well known American publication is Studies of the Genus Delphinium, 1931, by Earle I. Wilde, as Bulletin 519 of the Cornell University Agricultural Experiment Station.

The earliest special American publication from the horticultural point of view was a journal, For Better Delphiniums, begun in 1923, by Newell F. Vanderbilt, published in San Rafael, California, twice yearly. This magazine exerted much influence among enthusiasts for these plants, and soon its place was taken by the bulletins of the American Delphinium Society, of which Mr. Vanderbilt was the progenitor and which is now a strong active organization with large membership. The subsequent publications of this Society are important, as well as those of the British Delphinium Society, from 1930. There are no Delphinium societies in Italy, France, Belgium, Holland, Scandinavia, nor am I aware of them in other countries.

In 1936 appeared the suggestive contribution in Genetica, a journal published in Holland, on The Origin of New Forms in Delphinium, from the cytologist's point of view by W. J. C. Lawrence of the John Innes Horticultural Institution in England. Undoubtedly we shall learn much of the genetical development of delphinium, as of other plants, by cytological studies. In such reports, in general, chromosome findings are naturally cited from many authors as bases for conclusions. One wonders, in the absence of assurances from the cited authors, whether great care was exercised by them in the botanical determination of the plants under examination and also whether herbarium specimens of the plants were preserved so that the findings can be

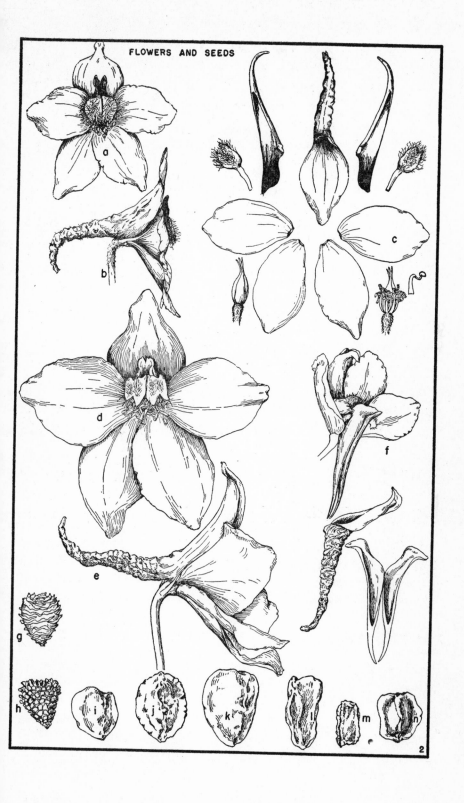

checked as the taxonomist always desires to check the opinions of workers as new evidences accrue. If a worker states that *Delphinium elatum* is a tetraploid, the successor is entitled to know where the plants came from, particularly whether native or cultivated, and whether they belonged to any one of the dozen or so natural variants of the species that have been described and named, and whether a competent authority identified the plants; otherwise there is no guaranty.

On the species of delphinium we have one general treatment in modern time, by E. Huth (1854–1897) of Frankfort-an-der-Oder, in Engler's Botanische Jahrbücher, 1895. This paper comprises 176 pages and accounts for more than 200 species. It is not drawn from the horticulturist's point of view. Its mode of nomenclature does not agree with present practice. In Annals of the Royal Botanic Garden, Calcutta, 1896, P. Brühl, friend of Huth, discusses delphinium (and other plants) "from India and adjacent regions," with portraits of some of them. There is apparently an overlapping of dates in these two publications, inasmuch as Huth, supposedly the earlier, cites Brühl by page and plate in a few instances.

In 1900 appeared Native and Garden Delphiniums of North America, with a key, by the late K. C. Davis (1867–1938) in Minnesota Botanical Studies. It comprises an account of fifty-two species and many botanical varieties. This is the first work of the kind in North America, and also the last monograph of all the native species, although a good number of contributions have appeared on certain groups or sections of the genus.

We are now ready to set forth. I shall endeavor to analyze our thesis, which is: to comprehend delphinium as a cultivated plant.

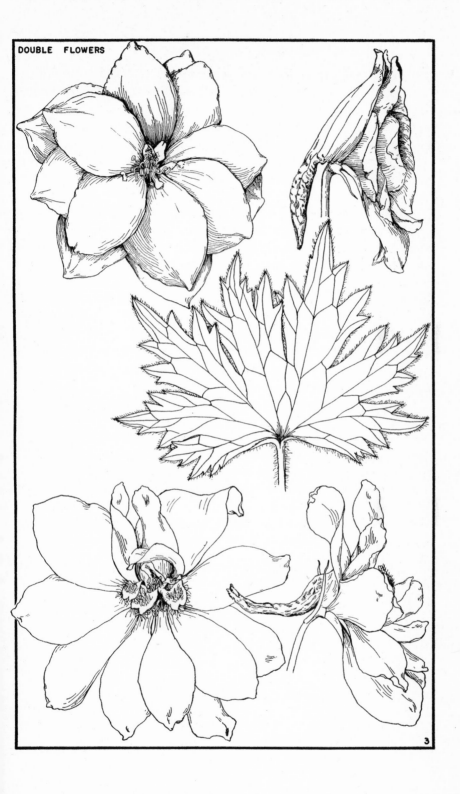

DOUBLE FLOWERS

3

The Delphinium Plant

THE DELPHINIUM is a noteworthy subject both in the wild and in cultivation. Habit of the plant is singular, with erect and usually straight stem crowned by terminal shapely and handsome flowers held free above the foliage. Form of the flower is peculiar, comprising a flying spur and a bell or bowl of highly colored parts, presenting a charming irregularity. Although the plant is closely kin to columbine and monkshood, yet the flower form is so marked and constant that it cannot be mistaken. I have never known a gardener, any more than a botanist, to mistake a delphinium for any other plant.

These features commend the plant to the grower, particularly if he is a plant-lover rather than only a color connoisseur. He should desire to maintain the flower pattern even though he may wish to enlarge it, to prolong its lasting quality, and perhaps to modify its color. He should hardly wish so to breed the flower as to eliminate the spur, for example, even if in so doing he develops a strange shape or a bizarre color. A delphinium without a spur is no longer a proper larkspur, and the singular character is lost. One's choice amongst the modified delphiniums, therefore, is good indication whether one is willing to learn the first great lesson in gardening, which is to desire the forms and structures nature has provided.

Much has been accomplished in recent years in breeding new races, so much so that many of the natural lines between species have been broken, and confusion in definition has resulted. It is a question whether the best result in any group of plants, in the long run, is not to be acquired by ameliorating a given species rather than by hybridizing it with other species and thereby losing the accomplishment of nature through the centuries.

The genus delphinium ranges far and wide over the northern hemisphere, and a few species in Africa reach beyond the equator. About 500 species have been described, although some of the names may be approximate duplicates. Many of them are plants of high mountains and are adapted to rock-gardens and alpine-gardens, although this utilization of them is little stressed. There is a class of them in Tibet and western China, represented by the true *Pylzowii*, of very dwarf habit and strikingly large brilliant flowers that some day will test the skill of trained rock-gardeners. Others of the species are good subjects for borders and wild gardens, and fanciers' collections, even though our present interest is confined to a few horticultural lines.

The North American delphiniums, of which about 110 species have been described, have yielded no horticultural races unless *D. nudicaule* is now contributing itself to some of the new Reds. These many species range from Florida and Mexico to Alaska, most abundant west of the Mississippi. Among them are probably 60 species well worth the care of the attentive grower; about one-half that number has been introduced to cultivation in their own country at one time or another, and the kinds are described in the Enumeration. When we have learned how to grow and to utilize them we shall be conscious of new interests in larkspurs and shall hope for novel developments; perhaps we shall not reach that state until we are able to absolve ourselves for the moment from the traditional conception of delphinium culture.

Many species of delphinium are weedy annuals without beauty for gardens. These are mostly inhabitants of drier parts of the Old World. There is no obligation to cultivate them.

If the novice is anxious to learn at once how to grow delphiniums, let him wait. I shall come to that important part in my own time, but there are other matters he should learn first. He should be filled with the desire to grow them; to this end, his information should be enlarged. Good gardening begins in the head.

The delphinium plant is annual, biennial, short-lived or long-lived perennial. The annual species best known in cultivation are *D. Ajacis, cardiopetalum, Consolida, divaricatum, orientale, paniculatum*. These are slender plants with fibrous thin roots.

The biennials are few and little known in cultivation with us. *D. Staphisagria*, and its relative *Requienii*, are sometimes grown. Seeds sown this year should produce blooming plants next year; then the plants die. Sometimes the short-lived showy perennial *D. grandiflorum* is treated as biennial (or even as annual), being rooted up after its second year; if seeds are sown in early spring it will bloom the first year as well as the second year and later.

Perennial delphiniums are of two cultural classes: those that grow or remain vigorous all the season, with very leafy stems and usually tall, and bloom from early summer to autumn, including the Garland and Candle larkspurs and also many native and other species not yet ameliorated; the tuberous-rooted or fleshy-rooted spring-blooming kinds that die to the ground after seeding and remain dormant from late spring or early summer to the following spring; many native species are in this group, as *D. tricorne, Menziesii, bicolor, carolinianum, decorum, Parishii, Parryi, simplex, variegatum, Andersonii, cardinale, Hanseni, hesperium, nudicaule, trolliifolium*, as well as the Asian *Zalil*. These remarks on season are made primarily for plants growing under natural conditions in the wild. In fertile soil with plenty of moisture under cultivation some of these species may cover a longer season. In nature *D. nudicaule* may send up a late cluster if the plant has been browsed; but in this group of species late or midsummer flowering is the exception.

If the reader has raised live-stock on the Plains or westward he knows the larkspur plant is poisonous to cattle that feed on it, and sheep may also react. This accounts for such names as Stagger-weed, Cow-poison, Poison-weed.

I have said that the flower of delphinium is peculiar. This statement is more than a flow of the pen. Inasmuch as I cannot expect my reader to have a fresh delphinium flower before him, I am obliged to resort to pictures, and these will be found in Plate 2. I trust the pictures and this text will stimulate the reader to separate a flower into its parts; the exercise is simple and should not take as much time as to burn a cigarette or to curl the hair. A hand-lens will help, but the parts are not as small as a needle's eye.

See the flower in side view, in profile the portraitest would say, Plate 2, *b, e*. It is enlarged, for the ease of eyes not trained to look pleasantly at parts of objects less than an inch long. The spur is too obvious to be overlooked. Note that it is an elongation from one of the petal-like parts of the flower, seen well in the upper central *c*. But the part is really a sepal, and the showy external part is all calyx rather than corolla as it is in most other flowers with which we are familiar. The sepals are five, the blades or expanded part being much alike but yet not duplicates. The calyx is frequently finely pubescent outside, although this condition is not likely to be noted until the attention is called to it; a small lens brings it out. The sepals commonly fall separately and practically simultaneously, usually much too soon for the comfort of the decorator: one of the desiderata in delphinium breeding is to lengthen the life of the flower.

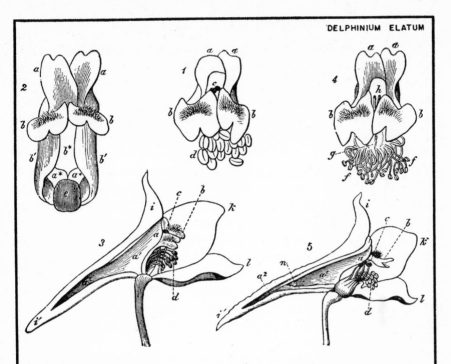

1. Young flower after removal of the petaloid calyx; front view. 2. The petals in their natural position, seen obliquely from in front and below. 3. Young flower, after removal of the right side of the calyx, seen from the right side. 4. Older flower, after removal of the calyx, front view. 5. Young flower, after removal of the right side of the calyx and corolla, seen from the right side. *a a*, The two upper petals, which are prolonged backwards into two spurs (a^1 a^2) that secrete and contain nectar (*n*), and which in front form an entrance for the humble-bee's proboscis; a^* a^*, bases of the same; *b b*, the two lower petals, of which the closely apposed surfaces form the lower boundary of the entrance for the humble-bee's proboscis; the upper surface of each bears a tuft of yellow hairs to serve as a nectar-guide, while between their claws (2. b' b') is an interval (2. b^*) in which the anthers and stigmas successively appear (in the two stages of flowering), and which is in the path of the insect's proboscis; *c*, dehisced anthers placed behind the entrance to the spur in the path of the insect's proboscis; *d*, anthers which have not yet dehisced, and are bent downwards over the female organs; *e*, surface of attachment of the stamens and carpels (which have been removed); *f*, withered stamens bent downwards; *g*, ovaries; *h*, stigmas, which have placed themselves in the same spot that the ripe anthers occupied in the first stage; *i*, left half of the upper sepal, prolonged backwards into a corrugated sheath (*i'*) for the spur; *k*, left lateral sepal; *l*, left lower sepal. (3 and 5 natural size; 1, 2, and 4 enlarged.)—*From Mueller.*

Inside the showy calyx is the "bee": note the center in *a* and *d*. This is not an intruding animal but the corolla, composed of a cluster of short oddly fashioned petals, usually four of them or four united by their bases into a single structure. The size, shape, color and hairiness of the petals afford good marks of distinction between species, and they are always important also to the discriminating horticulturist.

The upper two petals are prolonged into a single or a duplicate spur that runs back into the big sepal spur: you will need to open the big spur carefully to see them and to pull them out. These inner spurs are nectaries, to which we shall return in a forthcoming paragraph. You may see them separated in *c* Plate 2, on the upper corners, two of them; they were contained in the sepal spur seen in the center. In *f* top, the two spurs are seen hanging naked, the sepal spur being shown beneath after removal; and the two petal spurs are detached at lower right.

The upper petals are often similar in color to the sepals, yet in the true Candle larkspurs they are dark purple, almost black; in the true Garland larkspurs they are light or yellowish in color: so we have the black-eyed and the yellow-eyed blossoms. I use the word "true" on purpose, for in many of the highly developed garden delphiniums the parentages have been so mixed up that we do not know the breeds with which we are jockeying.

The two lower petals often present shapes and colors of their own, and they are likely to bear tufts or areas of long prominent hairs, or, in more technical language, are bearded. You may see the lower petals at upper right and left in *c*, Plate 2; and they are apparent in the lower part of the bee in *a* and *d*. Sharp observation of Plate 4 also discloses these and other parts.

Hidden behind the lower petals is the close cluster of stamens, ten or more of them; soon they begin to protrude, and you may see them in the bee at *a* and *d*, Plate 2, and again in Plate 4; the big anthers are prominent. Behind and above the stamens are the pistils, one to five of them according to the species. You may see them at the lower right (and left) in *c*, Plate 2, with the stamens about them; and a stamen is separated just to the right. The pistils ripen into the seedpods or follicles. The delphinium flower, or at least that of the usual species is proterandrous, the anthers maturing in advance of the pistils; this fact is important in fertilization, insuring cross-pollination.

The pod or follicle is a single carpel splitting at maturity down the inner or ventral suture, then discharging the many seeds. In the Rocket larkspur the follicle is normally one, but there may be two or three in variously doubled garden races. In the other most commonly cultivated larkspurs the follicles are three. If you have no fruiting piece of larkspur at hand, you may discover the follicles in Plates 6, 7, 8, 19, 20, 22, 23; they are interesting and decorative objects.

Seeds are packed one above the other in each carpel or follicle. If you have sown seeds of delphinium you may have noticed differences in the kinds. The seeds are usually somewhat longer than broad when ripe, but of different shape and configuration between the species. In some species the surface is squamate,—covered with scales or plates. You will need a strong hand-lens and good light to see them properly. At the bottom of Plate 2 some of them are displayed.

We have learned that the nectar is secreted at the end of the petal spurs that are hidden deep in the big calyx spur. Nectar is sought by humming-birds and insects; in extracting it the bird or bee may carry pollen to the next flower it visits, and cross-pollination may result. Irregular flowers, particularly those bearing spurs or sacs, are accounted entomophilous, pollinated by insects. Not all the insect visitors accomplish the act of pollination; in delphinium a long proboscis is required to reach the nectar, and an insect with short mouth-parts may cut the spur and take the nectar without paying for it. If one is interested in insects it is good entertainment to watch the visitors to larkspur flowers and to observe which ones perform the office legitimately. One is likely to see enough to reward the patience: thus, the late critical Charles Robertson (1858–1935) of Carlinsville, Illinois, in his Flowers and Insects mentions nineteen species of insects visiting *Delphinium tricorne* alone.

If the reader wishes to learn something about the mechanism of insect pollination he may study Plate 4, which is taken (by permission) from Handbook of Flower Pollination published by the Oxford Press, translated by J. R. Ainsworth Davis from the German of Paul Knuth. The picture represents *Delphinium elatum*. I am the more willing to insert this picture because it shows in detail the structure of a delphinium flower, about which I have been writing. The picture itself is accredited by Knuth to Hermann Müller. The legend under the cut is direct from the book but is here set in type of my choosing.

All this long discussion about the structure of the delphinium flower is important to one who wishes to hybridize. The pistils are to receive only the desired pollen, applied to the stigmatic part at the top of each of the styles. The operator must be sure that no other pollen reaches the pistil. This means the stamens of that flower must be cut away to guard against possible self-pollination; as the pistils mature late, the bare or emasculated flower should be covered with a cloth or thin paper bag, tightly tied, to wait for the stigmas to become receptive. When stigmas are ready, pollen may be brought from the chosen staminate parent on a knife point or a brush and dusted on them; then the bag should be replaced until the seeds ripen. In the meantime, the flower providing the pollen also should have been covered to forestall admixture of pollen on its anthers by a visiting insect. The real investigator attaches tags to the seed bags for the purpose of keeping records.

Thus far we have examined normal or natural flowers, but in cultivation the blossoms may become double. Effects of doubling are seen in Plate 3. At top is a regular double flower, front and side view. Petals and stamens still are intact, but extra whorls of sepals have arisen, all of the same shape. At bottom is an irregular double, front and side view, also a leaf to show that it belongs to the Candle or Elatum group. This flower was more than three inches across; larger ones are reported. It is one of the contemporaneous flopsy blossoms, with long petals of thin texture. Probably the two or three upper very narrow elements in the center represent extra petals, and it will be noted that the lower petals are three instead of two.

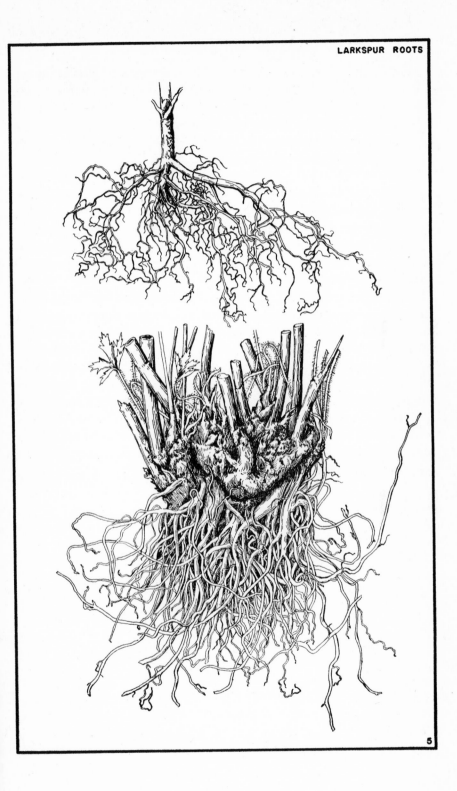

The Breeding of Delphiniums

WE FIND OURSELVES now confronted by an excessive range of variation in the cultivated delphiniums, particularly in the Candle group. Most of the variables have arisen within the last twenty-five years as the result of stimulated interest in their cultivation in widely separated regions and of many successful crosses between races and also between separate species. The variations, in the perennial species, are not fixed, to come true to seed, and usually do not yet merit the definition of horticultural varieties. They are races or strains, each one perhaps yielding a characteristic but indefinite progeny when propagated by seeds. The only way as yet to maintain particular kinds is by vegetative or asexual propagation. I see little hope in establishing seed-pure varieties from the extensive ranges of variations in the present breeding grounds.

This is not to say that the breeding operations are futile or even unpromising. The capabilities of the plants are being exhibited in the work, and great progress is evident in the production of larger flowers, better clusters or spikes, wide ranges of colors, stronger plants, seasonal adaptations. By these breeding efforts the delphinium has now taken its place as a major horticultural subject. Stocks are available in large quantities. Delphinium connoisseurs have arisen. We now need thoroughgoing scientific experiments in the breeding of delphiniums.

A scientific experiment requires clear vision of the results to be desired and positive permanent records of every step in the project. This means careful technique by a person definitely trained in breeding research.

The breeding may be straight seed selection year by year from promising plants, with the idea of producing good stocks that can be named and accurately described. It may mean hybridization to stimulate new variations, after which seed selection may proceed. The annual Rocket larkspur now has many varieties that come sufficiently true from seed; there is no reason why perennials should not have similar capabilities if we are willing to wait. It may mean definite undertakings in the direction of disease resistance. The process of continued selection after crossing may be more important than the crossing itself; in fact, selection is the major effort in breeding. I know of no published results of scientific breeding in delphiniums.

We do not yet know how closely seedlings of delphinium crosses follow Mendelian expectations. To determine this point many seeds must be sown and the seedlings grown to maturity, and expert calculations by unit characters must be made and recorded.

If the breeder is to hybridize delphiniums he should naturally begin with compatibles; or at least he should endeavor to determine whether there are compatibles and incompatibles in the genus. To ascertain these facts, experiments should start with true species; and the plants should be grown long enough under conditions of control from insects to be sure that one has pure lines with which to begin. Chromosome characteristics in the dividing nucleus of the cells should be determined of all the stock, and herbarium specimens should be preserved from plants under test to make sure that identifications are correct. Records picked up here and there from literature may mean little or nothing. It is unsafe to draw conclusions from them, although this is yet, unfortunately, a cytological practice. Species of delphinium are often difficult to determine, and in breeding work one should not depend on garden labels or seed-packet names or inexpert identifications.

Soon the careful investigator will develop lines of possibilities and the subject will begin to have reasons, with elements of prediction in it. If one wants a yellow delphinium carrying certain other qualities in combination, the breeder should have suggestions for a procedure. We may not expect precision in breeding, but we can at least overcome haphazard.

One disability is the lack of taxonomic authorities in the genus delphinium. The genus has not been critically studied as a whole since Huth, more than forty years ago, nor the American species since Davis in 1900. In the meantime much new material has accumulated, many species have been founded, and taxonomic methods have become more exact. There must be some kind of working procedure between taxonomists and breeders.

It is not possible by chromosome studies to determine the parentage of old varieties yet in cultivation, for such studies cannot be made on preserved materials but only in living cells, and we cannot be certain that living plants now called by a given varietal name are genetically the same as the ones introduced under that name many years ago, considering the confusions in horticultural practice and the probability of other crosses having taken place in the meantime. However, we might soon arrive at an estimate of the probable parentage by systematic investigation of behaviors of many contemporaneous crosses or mutations in the genus.

Investigations of the kind I have suggested are hardly commercial. They must be projected and maintained as a scientific adventure. Lacking such an enterprise, the commercial men and the amateurs may continue to cross and to sow seeds, and we shall watch the progeny with sympathetic interest. We are sure many of the types in the future, as in the past, will yield superb results. If the new ones are not always superior to the old, we shall at least have the stimulus of novelty and anticipation.

Let it be noted that a plant called a hybrid in horticultural literature may not be a cross. The word is likely to be employed loosely in the sense of "ameliorated" or "improved"; it presumably has commercial value. Nor are we to accept an uncritical attitude of botanists that all cultivated plants are mixed up by hybridization. Probably the role of species-hybridization in the origin of strange forms both in the garden and in the wild is over emphasized. In the present article I have spoken of hybridization in its precise meaning, to designate the results of actual manipulated recorded crossing.

The Cultivation of Delphiniums

AFTER THIS LONG WAIT, we are ready to consider the growing of delphiniums. The beginner may approach the subject with confidence, because the kinds commonly raised present no peculiar difficulties. Other advice will be found in the succeeding chapters devoted to the five main groups, so that the discussion at this point may be brief.

Perhaps the reader should be told he is not to expect in a book of this kind to be entertained by experiences of all the details of cultivation and discussion of varieties and local successes that are such essential parts of periodicals, personal letters, and yearbooks of societies. The present writing is rather a background treatment of the subject, and it ought to aid in directing the discussions of gardeners and nurserymen and societies among themselves. A book cannot anticipate the problems and personal difficulties as well as successes of individual growers; these experiences are always to be repeated year by year.

The common delphiniums thrive in any ordinary garden land if it is well drained and at the same time does not suffer from dryness. Proper fertilizing for vegetable-garden crops should be acceptable to delphiniums. The soil should not be decidedly acid, but of a neutral reaction.

Land should be well conditioned in the first place. If rough and not in full tilth, it should be dug deep with spade or fork, and all big stones, hard clods, old grass clumps, and remaining roots should be removed. A liberal cover of old manure may be spaded under, or a decayed compost of leaves and straw. Addition of prepared chemical fertilizer is advantageous. Most of the fertilizers are only slowly soluble and little result may be noted from them the first year if they are merely sprinkled on the surface, except, perhaps, when moisture is abundant and continuous. In plantations of established perennials the less soluble fertilizers, as bonemeal and muriate of potash, may be applied twelve to eighteen inches deep in three or four holes punched into the ground about the stools.

Perhaps the location is more important than the land. As most of the familiar delphiniums are tall and slender plants, they need protection from rampaging winds. In the lee of a hedge, as of evergreens, is suitable location provided the ground is not already too full of permanent roots. In front of berry bushes, and other tall strong stuff, should be good location. The bloom is also shown off to advantage against a background, which may well be a fence of pleasing design. Partial shade in the hotter parts of summer days is great aid in keeping the plants in vigor and in prolonging the blooming season. Whenever soils tend to suffer from drought, facilities for watering (not sprinkling) are to be provided; and for exhibition bloom, preparation for irrigation may be installed.

In autumn, the ground should be mulched with clean material that does not mat and is not the carrier of weeds if perennial species are grown. Excelsior is often advised. Autumn leaves mixed with twigs and clean straw or other coarse material to prevent packing are also advisable. For myself, I like coarse threshed straw; and if it is left on in spring, the area has a cool and covered look and is clean to the feet. I like to apply good chemical or prepared fertilizer in autumn before the mulch is laid. If tillage is required the following season because the ground is hard or crusty, the mulch is easily raked to one side and then applied again; or it may be retained until autumn. The grower soon learns how to meet requirements of soil and seasons. Every garden is a new experiment. Profuse flowering and vigorous plants are obtained only on fertile land and with continuous moisture; and, to start with, the plants should be young and fresh and of good constitution.

If the site is well chosen, there is little necessity to stake and tie the plants; yet if one grows very tall strains of Candle larkspur and particularly for exhibition purposes, well chosen inconspicuous supports may be hidden behind the big stalks and the tying may be accomplished so neatly as hardly to be noticed. A clump of stalks from a single crown may often be supported by a cord tied around them and secured to a single stake at one side; sometimes the combined strength of all the stalks will hold them without the stake. It is the highly developed heavy-headed type of perennial delphinium that is most in need of staking. Some of the strains bear so many flowers of large size that hard rains are likely to bear them down and to ruin the blossoms then open.

Further discussion on growing larkspurs may be reserved for the

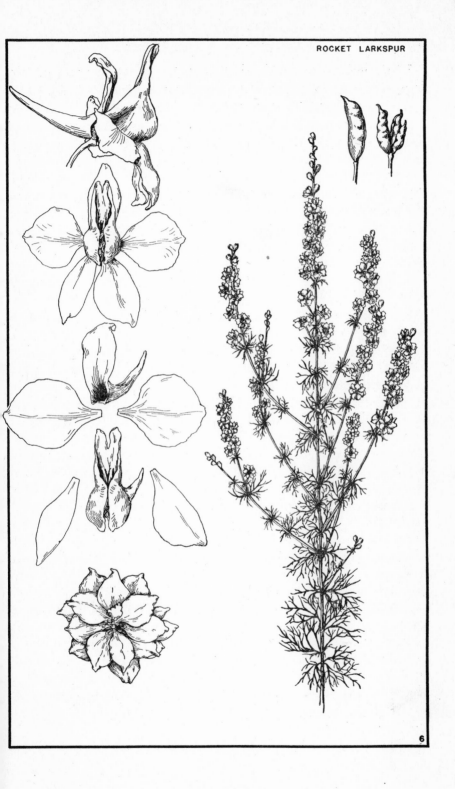

6

different groups,—Rockets and Forking which are annuals, Bouquet which are often treated as biennials although perennial, Garland and Candle, perennial. At those points the propagation of the plants is considered.

Aside from these horticultural classes are the many distinct species, or "botanicals," which are so various among themselves that uniform advice cannot be applied. The low-country species, as *D. carolinianum*, *D. virescens*, should thrive in common borders if allowed the root room they need. Some of them require a moister soil, although not wet, as *D. tricorne*. Bear in mind the distinctions between the summer-dormant and summer-growing species as discussed on page 10. The habits of the species should be learned when the stock is purchased.

The mountain species, from western North America, are often at home in the usual garden, if not too hot. The alpines require the attention of the real rock-gardener, but they may not be expected to thrive in the arid piles of stones and slabs popularly supposed to be rock-gardens. In some cases of native species, seeds may not germinate the first year; two or more years may be required.

The alpine larkspurs are little understood by cultivators in this country, yet there is much promise in them. Sampson Clay in his Present-Day Rock Garden (London 1937) writes: "Even amongst the dwarf species of high places there are, however, plants that can make two-guinea novelties look to their laurels for sheer showiness, and drive them beaten from the field of colour."

The making of rock-gardens is not discussed in this book, and there appears to be little experience with delphiniums for them in this country. One may find kinds mentioned, either here or abroad, for such uses, but it does not follow that the species are actually in cultivation. Observations may have been made on plants in the wild, or accounts may have been taken from botanical books or writings of travellers. There is opportunity for interesting experiences with rock-garden larkspurs, even in regions where rock-gardening is difficult for climatic reasons.

The delphinium grower in other countries would be disappointed at the brief attention accorded to named horticultural varieties of delphinium, if he should see this book. Such varieties are few in North American lists, and roots of European kinds are not regularly importable. In other countries certificates may be awarded meritorious novelties, and much is made of them in shows. In America delphinium culture has run so strongly to the Candle class that other groups have been relatively neglected. The named varieties of perennial larkspur naturally fall into the Bouquet, Garland or Candle groups. Alphabetic or other lists of recommended garden varieties in other countries may not distinguish the group or class to which the plants belong, so the subject is often unclarified. On the subject of varieties Leonian writes: "In our country, named delphiniums are not featured because, in the first place, there is ready sale for mere seedlings at attractive prices; and in the second place, most of our climatic conditions are such as to render the life of delphiniums a short one and the value of named varieties rather dubious."

Growing delphiniums for bloom under glass is practiced to some extent. Continuous winter bloom with perennial species is seldom attained unless one has an adaptable variety or strain, and such strains are not regularly on the market. Certain persons have developed a strain of their own for such purposes, and have acquired the skills necessary for success. In general, if glasshouse work is attempted, it is expected to have bloom in late April and in May in the North. Seeds of *D. grandiflorum* sown in October should yield plants in bloom in April; earlier sowing of the seeds does not hasten the blooming period, probably because of insufficient light intensity in the short months. Seeds of *D. Ajacis* may be sown in October or later for early and late spring bloom. Belladonna larkspurs have not responded to winter cultivation, although experiments by Harold E. White, Massachusetts State College (reported in Society for Horticultural Science 1935, p. 653) have given bloom November to January as result of special storage conditions. Roots of perennial Candle larkspurs may be lifted in autumn and stored at temperature above freezing until January, and then brought in for bloom, but results are not likely to be commercially profitable. One must be careful not to breed the rot diseases. Temperature for delphiniums under glass should be about 50° until they are well toward the blooming stage. See, also, Kenneth Post, Cornell University, in Book of the American Delphinium Society for 1936, page 49.

All the foregoing remarks on cultivation of larkspurs are drawn from common experience. This does not mean that the directions are sufficient. We shall become more exacting in the growing and shall need to know the particular roles of lime and phosphorus and other constituents in the soil. Inquiries are under way in these and similar subjects, and we shall learn in due time. It is to be remembered, however, that the more exact our knowledge from researches the more intimately must each of us know his own soil and conditions if the results are to be accurately applied.

The grower of larkspurs of any kind must be constantly on the lookout for diseases and pests and be able to meet them. This requires careful observation so that one may know what one looks at. It is satisfaction to present two good articles on these subjects in this book. The diseases are treated by Leon H. Leonian, professor in the University of West Virginia at Morgantown, delphinarian and author of the word, Editor for the American Delphinium Society. The insects and related pests are handled by W. E. Blauvelt, professor in the College of Agriculture at Cornell University, who is keen in economic entomology.

Diseases of Delphinium

Leon H. Leonian

Sturdy larkspurs in old gardens may seem to be incapable of disease, but the improved kinds in highly tilled plantations may invite trouble; and even the old ones may be the survivors of unnoticed disasters. The modern delphinium grower must be alert to the risks.

Damping-off

This disease is caused by a number of soil-inhabiting fungi, especially Pythium and Rhizoctonia, and constitutes a limiting factor in the successful propagation of delphiniums from seeds. There are two types of damping-off: pre-emergence and post-emergence. In case of the first type of the disease the seedlings are attacked and destroyed before they push their way through the soil; those that escape may be attacked after they emerge. But once the true leaves have formed there is very little danger of damping-off because at this stage the plants have developed a high degree of resistance.

Damping-off fungi are universally present in all garden soils, and may or may not manifest themselves, depending on environmental conditions. Cool season, good aeration, and efficient soil drainage may keep the disease in check under outdoor conditions, but in order to insure a good crop of seedlings it is necessary to sterilize the soil and to treat the seed. Formalin treatment of the soil is the most satisfactory. A 5 percent solution of formalin (5 parts of formalin in 95 parts of water) is poured over the soil until it is completely saturated. Two or three days later when the soil is somewhat dry, it is turned and aerated. This is repeated every day for at least ten days until all odor of formalin has disappeared. Organic mercury dusts such as Semesan, or copper oxide such as Cuprocide, should be shaken with delphinium seeds before planting; these substances check any organism that may be present on the seed.

Botrytis rot (Botrytis cinerea)

Although ordinarily a weak parasite, this fungus becomes very destructive to delphinium seedlings when conditions are favorable for its growth. Overcrowding, poor air circulation and an abundance of moisture enable the fungus to destroy a great many plants. It first attacks the petioles and such parts of the leaves as touch the soil, but soon it spreads to the crown. The work of destruction is so rapid that within a few days the entire crop in a flat may be lost. The most effective method of control is to transplant the seedlings before they become overcrowded. Occasional dusting with sulfur or spraying with bordeaux mixture (2-4-50) is recommended.

As a general rule, larger plants are not attacked by Botrytis, although sometimes floral parts may be infected and an occasional seed-pod destroyed. Such seed-pods are easily recognized by a grayish fluffy substance, consisting largely of the spores of this fungus, on the surface of the pods.

Mildew (Erysiphe polygoni)

In many parts of the country mildew is not a serious factor in the growing of delphinium. But where cool and moist seasons prevail mildew becomes a major problem. The fungus remains on the surface of its host plant and only its feeding parts penetrate the cells to derive nourishment. The white powdery substance which characterizes the disease consists of the mycelium and the summer spores of the fungus. These spores are blown away by the wind to other plants and thus serve to spread the infection. Later in the season the winter spores form in small black pustules, and serve to carry the fungus over winter until the arrival of the spring when a new cycle of infection begins.

Delphiniums greatly vary in their resistance to mildew. For instance, *Delphinium cheilanthum, D. formosum, D. Maackianum*, and *D. tiroliense* have been reported to be very susceptible while *D. Ajacis, D. Consolida, D. grandiflorum* and *D. tatsienense* have been found to be very resistant, although other reports indicate that *D. Ajacis* and *D. Consolida* are very favorable hosts for the mildew. This indicates that either there are particular races of mildew in different parts of the country, or else resistance is controlled by environmental conditions.

The resistance of hybrid delphiniums to mildew varies from extreme susceptibility to a high degree of immunity. The more susceptible sorts may be completely covered with the mildew, fail to attain any size, become deformed, and eventually die. In some cases, mildew is confined largely to one part of the plant, such as the stem, or the leaves, or the sepals of the flower.

Much effort has been devoted to the production of immune varieties

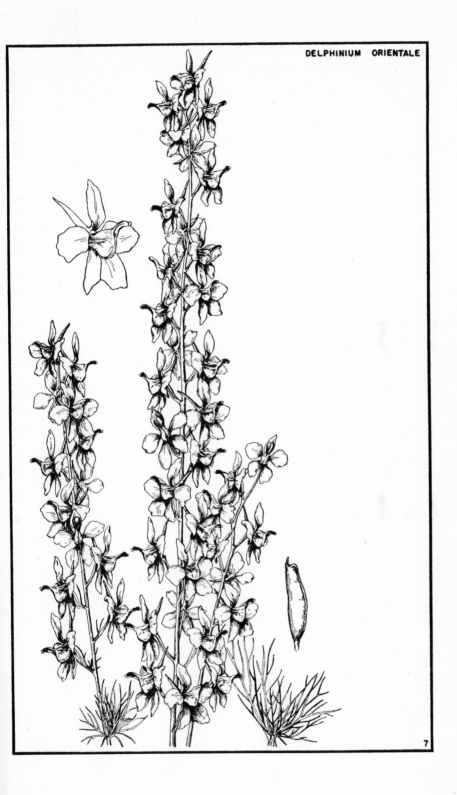

of delphinium, and a number of such plants have been placed on the market. However, there is evidence to show that a given plant may be highly resistant to mildew in one locality, but may become susceptible under other environmental conditions.

Dusting with sulfur or spraying with bordeaux will keep the mildew down.

Bacterial leaf-spot, black-spot (Phytomonas delphinii)

This disease manifests itself in the form of black irregular spots especially on the leaves, although the petioles, stems, buds, and even the sepals may also be infected. Leaf-spot is not fatal, is prevalent usually during cool seasons, and does not attack all species or varieties with equal force. Some varieties are highly resistant, others very susceptible. The latter have their leaves peppered with black spots, and often the spikes are deformed. There is no adequate control measure against the disease, although spraying with bordeaux has been recommended by some persons.

Bacterial crown-rot (Bacillus destructans)

A sudden wilting of apparently vigorous and healthy plants characterizes this disease. A wilted plant may be easily pulled up exposing blackened, decayed, and usually ill-smelling basal portions. The organism confines its activity to the crown but gradually penetrates into the roots. Once infection sets in, there is no hope for the plant. Chemical treatments are not effective because the bacteria are systemic in the tissues and cannot be reached by disinfectants. Very rarely is the organism capable of affecting the aerial portions, and the writer has observed only one such case. The upper part of a young spike was infected and had been reduced to a soft putrid mass.

This organism is universal in its distribution and causes soft rots of many roots, tubers and bulbs of flowers and vegetables. In northern parts of the United States, in Canada, and at high elevations where conditions are ideal for the growth of delphinium this disease is not known; but where summers are long, warm, and muggy, the crown-rot is prevalent and highly destructive. After one or two years growth the plants succumb. It may be of interest to state that a young delphinium may be planted in the very spot where an old one died by the crown-rot, and thrive. The critical period in the life of delphinium is either at the time or shortly after the greatest display of flowers. Apparently the production of a large crop of flowers exhausts the plants and breaks down their resistance.

There are no control measures against this organism. Those who live under conditions less favorable to delphinium should be content with the biennial habit of their plants.

Sclerotium rot (Sclerotium delphinii)

This is perhaps the most dreaded disease of delphiniums. The causal organism lives in the soil and is capable of attacking a great many perennials such as aconitum, antirrhinum, aquilegia, calendula, campanula, dahlia, hosta, iris, lilium, lobelia, penstemon, phlox, potentilla, pyrethrum, rudbeckia, stevia, tulipa, valeriana, veronica, and viola.

The disease is characterized by yellowing of the leaves and sudden wilting of the entire plant. Such plants are easily pulled up exposing decayed basal portions which do not have the putrid smell of plants affected with the bacterial rot. Often white threads may be seen on decayed parts and the adjoining soil; these are the vegetative parts of the fungus. If left undisturbed, the fungus forms small shot-like bodies at first white, later changing to tan and brown. These bodies are known as sclerotia and it is their function to carry the fungus over the winter. Immediate destruction of wilted plants with the adjoining soil is the most effective method of control against this disease. Where sclerotium rot is prevalent, no organic matter of any sort should be added to the soil because the fungus grows on it and thus spreads in the ground. Whenever a plant dies with this disease, the soil in an area of eighteen inches in diameter and twelve inches deep should be removed and replaced with fresh soil or even with sand. Enriched with commercial fertilizers, sand will support a good growth and form a barrier against advancing fungi because it does not have any organic matter with which to support fungus growth.

Soil treatment with mercuric chloride (1 part in 2,000) has been recommended, but this does not have much practical value because by the time the presence of the rot is suspected, the plant is too far gone to be saved.

Canker (Fusarium sp.)

This disease has been reported from Delaware, Florida, and West Virginia. Undoubtedly it occurs in other states. The first sign of the disease consists of a discolored sunken area on the stem, which extends downward very rapidly, reaches the crown and kills the plant. If a cankered stem is split open, a cottony mass filling the hollow region will be revealed. This is the vegetative part of the fungus and contains myriads of spores.

Spraying with bordeaux and cutting the spike off several inches below the canker before the fungus has reached the crown will save the plant.

Other fungus diseases

An Alternaria species causes black stem-canker in West Virginia; *Cercospora delphinii* and *Phyllosticta delphinii* causing leaf-spot are reported from Colorado; *Corticium vagum* is the cause of stem-rot in New York and Michigan. From Nebraska, Colorado, Montana, Idaho and Oregon have come reports of *Puccinia clematidis* causing rust, while smut, due to *Urocystis sorosporioides*, has been found in California. Undoubtedly many other diseases are present but have not been observed or reported as yet.

Virus diseases

Delphiniums are attacked by a number of virus diseases. Some of these manifest themselves by yellow streaks on the leaves, by mottling, and by stunting. Often, however, lime-induced chlorosis is confused with virus diseases. Too much lime in the soil prevents the plants from securing a sufficient amount of iron and consequently the leaves show a chlorotic condition. This may be remedied by the addition of soluble iron salts to the soil, while virus troubles remain unaffected by this treatment.

The most dreaded virus disease of delphinium is commonly known as "delphinium greens." Diseased plants remain stunted, the spikes fail to develop properly, and the buds, on opening, remain a sickly green and very small. Plants affected by this trouble cannot live very long and should be destroyed as soon as detected. This disease is prevalent in California, Washington, and Oregon, but only an occasional specimen has been found in some of the eastern states. Very little is known about the nature of this disease.

Pests of Delphinium

W. E. BLAUVELT

ALTHOUGH THE DELPHINIUM is subject to attack by a considerable number of pests as discussed below, these offer no serious difficulty to the successful culture of this splendid flower. All are amenable to control by the methods described, and a number of the most common pests, namely the red-spider mite, thrips, and aphids are susceptible to the same treatment—rotenone sprays. Other pests such as cut-worms, stem-borers, slugs, and sowbugs are likely to be troublesome only occasionally. The pallid mite is undoubtedly the most serious pest of delphinium in those areas where it is prevalent and for this reason special emphasis is given to measures against it.

Pallid mite (Tarsonemus pallidus)

The pallid mite, also known as the cyclamen mite, is a common and serious pest of delphiniums particularly in the northern states and Canada. The Rocket larkspur, although susceptible, is seldom infested.

The characteristic symptoms of pallid mite injury are distortion and blackening of the leaves and buds. The mites infest the young developing leaf and blossom tissues and feed by puncturing the plant cells with minute bristle-like mouthparts and sucking up the fluid cell contents. Varying degrees of injury occur. When the mites are very numerous the developing leaves are severely curled upward, twisted, swollen, and blackened. The blossom spikes are "blasted" and remain as gnarled clumps of stunted deformed buds, purplish-black in color. When the mites are few the leaves may exhibit only a moderate puckering of the basal part and the blossom spike may develop almost normally with only a few deformed discolored buds.

Because of the black discoloration and the fact that the mites are practically invisible to the naked eye, pallid mite injury is likely to be mistaken for disease symptoms and is sometimes confused with the bacterial leaf-spot of delphinium caused by *Phytomonas delphinii* and commonly known as "black-spot" or "black disease." However, the blackening from mite injury is more continuous or general and is superficial whereas the leaf-spot lesions are definite spots extending through the leaf, tarry-black on the upper surface and brown beneath. The bacterium does not cause distortion of the leaves and buds.

Pallid mites are so small they are barely visible to the naked eye as tiny moving specks. The adult female mites are oval, milky white to amber or brownish, and about one one-hundredth of an inch in length. The young are smaller, glistening white and rather slender. The eggs are oblong, oval, smooth, and translucent. The entire life cycle from egg to egg-laying female requires only about two weeks at temperatures of 70° to 80°.

The pallid mite has been recorded as attacking some thirty-five species of plants, in most instances under greenhouse conditions. It is a major pest of a number of greenhouse crops, notably cyclamen, saintpaulia, gerbera, and chrysanthemum. Out-of-doors it persists from year to year on delphinium, strawberry, and a number of perennial weeds and also particularly on purslane.

On delphinium plants out-of-doors the mites overwinter in the young shoots or buds on the crown of the plant often one-half inch or more below the soil surface. They are able to survive very severe winters. They resume feeding and laying eggs by early April in New York. Due to the short life cycle there are many generations in the course of the growing season. The mites are most active and destructive in the moderate temperatures of spring and fall and are checked by the higher temperatures and lower humidities of midsummer. The mites infest the young developing leaves and blossom buds which furnish a humid protected environment. They are seldom found exposed on older expanded leaves.

Control of the pallid mite is difficult. The mites reproduce rapidly, are resistant to insecticides, and live in such protected situations on the plant that many of them cannot be reached with insecticides.

If the delphinium planting is free from pallid mite, it is well worth taking considerable care to avoid introducing this destructive pest. The fact that mites cannot fly, are not transmitted on seed or in soil, and are probably rarely blown by the wind or carried by bees to any considerable distance, makes this entirely feasible in most cases. The pallid mite is almost invariably introduced in infested delphinium plants or other hosts. Whenever delphinium plants are purchased from growers or exchanged with friends, they should be examined

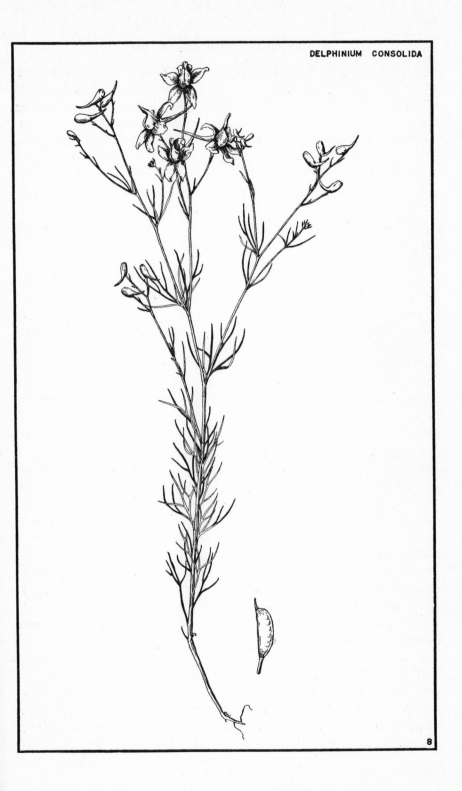

8

very carefully for symptoms of mite infestation before being placed in the garden. Since dormant stock with little or no foliage may exhibit no obvious symptoms of mite infestation, it is important to purchase such plants only with a guarantee of freedom from mite and to accept gifts only from gardens known to be free of the pest. If seedlings of delphinium are started in a greenhouse, they should be segregated as much as possible from other plants which may be infected with the mite.

If only an occasional plant is found to be infested with the pallid mite, the best procedure is to remove it before the mites have spread to the remainder of the planting, being careful not to bring the infested individuals in contact with neighboring plants in the process. If particularly valuable, these plants may be freed of mites by hot water treatment and replanted. The spacing of plants so the foliage does not touch aids greatly in preventing the spread of mites.

Although spray treatments cannot be relied on completely to free infested plants of mites due to their protected locations, yet repeated thorough applications of certain spray materials supplemented by the prompt removal and burning of infested shoots, have apparently been of some value in mite control.

Further experimental work is needed to determine the relative value of various materials for pallid mite control. On the basis of present information, it appears that rotenone sprays are more effective than nicotine or pyrethrum. Since the various brands of rotenone sprays on the market differ somewhat in the content of rotenone and other active ingredients, no single dilution can be recommended for all. The dilution recommended by the manufacturers for highly resistant pests should be tried. With brands that contain 1 to 1½ per cent rotenone, a dilution of 1 part to 250 parts of water (1 tablespoonful to 1 gallon) is usually satisfactory.

Spraying should start in early spring as soon as growth begins, or even before. The spray should be directed downward into the crown and the tips of the shoots and be applied liberally as a forceful spray. Spraying should be repeated at weekly intervals for at least several weeks and preferably until the flower-buds develop. Shoots that show evidence of pallid mite injury should be removed and burned as soon as noticed, taking care to avoid contact with neighboring plants. Finely ground sulfur kills many of the exposed mites and better control may be secured by either combining a wetable sulfur with the rotenone spray or following each spray treatment with an application of finely ground dusting sulfur.

The hot water treatment has proved a valuable means of cyclamen mite control. This is probably the only certain method of completely ridding infested plants of the pallid mite and if properly carried out will kill all stages of the mite without injury to the plant. The method is practical for the treatment of young delphinium plants in pots and may also be used for older plants that are being transplanted.

For delphinium seedlings in small pots immersion in water at 110° for fifteen minutes is sufficient. For larger plants in pots of four-inch or larger size, a twenty-five minute treatment is required to kill the mites that live between the leaf-bases in the crown. Twenty-five to thirty minutes is required for clumps dug from the field and the soil removed from the upper part of the crown.

Hot-water treatment on a small scale can be accomplished without any special equipment except a good thermometer. A large wash-boiler, garbage can, barrel, or even laundry tub may be used. Plants in pots are best handled in trays with slats or wire mesh bottoms and wire or strap handles. The treating tank is supplied with sufficient water of the right temperature (110° F.) more than to cover the plants. This is readily arranged by blending hot and cold water. A good thermometer is necessary. The plants are entirely immersed in the water and left for the required interval of time. During the treatment the water should be kept within a degree of the proper temperature throughout. This can be accomplished by stirring the water with a paddle and adding a little hot water at intervals to keep the temperature from dropping. For treatment of any considerable number of plants a good-sized tank is desirable. The water can be heated and kept to the proper temperature by steam run into the tank and controlled with a hand valve. The water can be agitated by a motor-driven propellor or with a paddle. For large-scale treatment special equipment with automatic temperature regulation and motor-driven agitator is best.

On removal from the water, pots should be tilted momentarily to drain water out of the tops. Plants should be shaded with sheets of newspaper for twenty-four to forty-eight hours after treatment. Every precaution should be taken to prevent them from becoming reinfested with mites after treatment. Soil particles on the foliage may be rinsed off immediately after treatment or after the shade is removed.

The broad mite (Tarsonemus latus)

The broad mite is closely related to the pallid mite and very similar in appearance but is much less injurious to delphinium and far simpler to control. Whereas the pallid mite infests the young developing leaves and buds and causes marked distortion of growth, the broad mite infests largely the already expanded leaves and causes no distortion aside from a slight downward cupping of the margins. The characteristic symptom of broad mite injury to delphinium is a shiny bronzed appearance of the lower leaf surface. On many of its host plants, the broad mite also attacks and frequently kills the terminal buds, but the writer has rarely seen injury of this type on delphinium. With aid of a good hand-lens, magnifying ten to fourteen diameters, broad mites can be distinguished from pallid mites by their shorter broader shape and more rapid movements. The eggs of the broad mite are strikingly different, being nearly round, flattened, and pearl colored with rows of white spots on the surface.

Control of the broad mite is simple, since it feeds on exposed surfaces and is susceptible to various insecticides. An effective method of control consists of dusting the plants with finely ground dusting sulfur. This is effective against all stages of the mite except the eggs, and the coating of sulfur will kill many of the young mites as they hatch. One light but thorough dusting will give a very high degree of control, but one or two additional applications a week or ten days apart may be advisable to insure a complete cleanup.

Rotenone sprays as suggested for the control of the pallid mite are also effective against the broad mite provided they are applied so as to cover the under side of the leaves.

Red-spider mite (Tetranychus telarius)

The red-spider mite is a rather common and injurious pest of delphinium, being particularly troublesome in periods of hot dry weather. Red-spider mite injury to delphinium appears as a characteristic dull gray stippled or mottled condition of the leaves caused by the innumerable feeding punctures of the mites. The infested areas are often covered with fine webbing spun by the mites. Badly infested leaves become functionless, then wilt and turn brown. The plants may be seriously stunted and weakened.

The mites are found largely on the under surface of the leaves. They are less than one-fiftieth inch in length when full grown and therefore rather inconspicuous even when numerous. Although commonly called "red-spider" they are mites, not spiders, and are seldom red. The general color effect to the naked eye is yellowish-green or grayish. In the fall the mites often become orange colored or red.

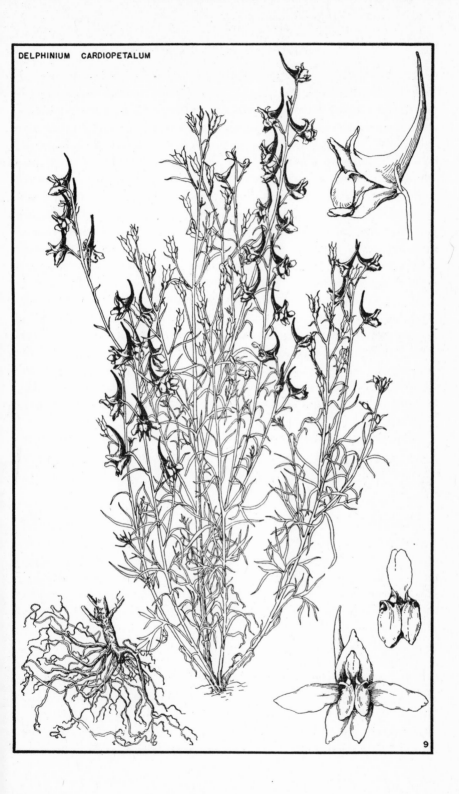

DELPHINIUM CARDIOPETALUM

9

The red-spider mite passes the winter as orange or red colored females under debris around the base of the plants and in the hollow stubs of stalks. There are many generations in the course of a season, as the life cycle is short. The red-spider mite is a common pest of numerous other greenhouse and garden flowers and breeds also on a variety of weeds and grasses from which the mites may migrate or be blown by wind to delphiniums.

Control may be difficult. The red-spider mite is resistant to many insecticides and is not satisfactorily controlled by nicotine or pyrethrum sprays. Rotenone sprays when used at a rather high concentration usually give satisfactory control and these are also effective and commonly employed for the control of thrips and aphids. For most brands, which contain about one per cent of rotenone, a dilution of 1 to 200 is suggested. This corresponds to 4 teaspoonfuls or 1⅓ tablespoonfuls to 1 gallon of water or 1 quart to 50 gallons. Since it is essential thoroughly to wet the under side of the leaves where most of the mites feed, one should use a spray rod with an angle nozzle to direct the spray upward.

Clean cultivation and close cutting of weeds in the vicinity of the planting are of value in reducing infestation by the red-spider mite.

Thrips

Several species of thrips attack delphinium and some of them cause marked injury. Thrips are inconspicuous slender-bodied active insects only about one-twentieth inch in length. They are colored yellow, light brown, or nearly black, depending on the species. They infest a great variety of plants and breed in numbers on various weeds and grasses.

Thrips infest both the under and upper surfaces of the leaves and the stems, buds, and blossoms as well. They feed by puncturing the epidermis, lacerating the cells, and sucking up the sap and green coloring matter. Injured foliage shows numerous small silvery bleached areas that later turn brown. On badly infested leaves the injured areas merge until the entire surface may be affected.

Control is accomplished by repeated applications of any of the standard contact sprays of nicotine, rotenone, or pyrethrum. Rotenone sprays, as recommended for the control of the pallid and red-spider mites are highly effective against thrips. Nicotine sulfate is effective in the proportions of 2 teaspoonfuls to 1 gallon of water with the addition of about 2 tablespoonfuls of soap flakes or powder. Nicotine-lime dust containing three or four per cent of nicotine gives good control. It is obtainable ready mixed and easily applied by means of hand or knapsack type dusters.

Aphids or plant-lice

Both perennial and annual larkspurs are sometimes infested by one or more species of aphids, commonly called plant-lice. They are small plump soft-bodied insects usually green in color. They cluster on the tender young growth and, if abundant, cause wilting and distorted growth. The foliage may be discolored by a sooty fungus which grows in the "honeydew" excreted by the aphids.

Control of aphids is by thorough application with contact sprays of nicotine, rotenone, or pyrethrum. Nicotine sulfate for small scale spraying is best used at the rate of 2 teaspoonfuls to 1 gallon of water with the addition of about 2 tablespoonfuls of soap flakes or powder to act as a spreading and wetting agent and to release nicotine vapor. Rotenone and pyrethrum sprays should be diluted according to manufacturers' directions or stronger if necessary.

Nicotine-lime dust containing three per cent of nicotine is very effective and may be applied with inexpensive hand dusters which are quicker and easier to operate than hand sprayers.

Stem-borers

Several species of boring caterpillars, notably the common stalk-borer and the burdock borer, at times cause considerable injury to delphinium. The borer usually enters the stem near the base and burrows upward, pushing out the "sawdust" through openings made at intervals. Injured stems often wilt or break over and die.

The natural food plants of these borers are various kinds of grasses and weeds, particularly ragweed and burdock. Eggs are deposited on the plants in autumn and hatch the following spring. Often about mid-summer many half-grown caterpillars migrate from the plants originally attacked to seek more succulent or larger stems in which to complete their development. At such times they may invade the garden and attack delphinium as well as a variety of other plants.

Control consists of preventive measures aimed at destroying the overwintering eggs and keeping down wild host plants near the garden. In late autumn all dead plant tops should be removed from the garden and burned. Weeds and tall grasses in the vicinity of the garden should be cut close, removed and burned. Areas close to the garden should be kept as free as possible of weeds and tall growing grasses.

If borers have entered delphinium plants and are discovered in time, the stalks may be saved by carefully slitting the infested part lengthwise and removing the borer, or stabbing through the stem with a row of pins mounted in a piece of soft wood. A concentrated solution of nicotine or pyrethrum injected through an opening in the burrow by means of an oil can is often effective.

Cutworms

Seedlings and newly transplanted young plants of delphinium are sometimes destroyed by cutworms. These are most common in the spring and early summer. Cutworms are smooth fleshy dull colored caterpillars that feed at night and during the day remain coiled up just under the surface of the ground. Their common method of attack is to chew through the stem at the ground level, causing the plant to fall over. On older plants they sometimes climb up the stems and feed on the foliage and buds. Stirring the soil around the injured plants will usually bring the culprits to light.

Control of cutworms, particularly in large gardens, is by the use of a poison bait. The following formula has given good results:

Wheat bran	2½ quarts
Paris green	2 level tablespoonfuls
Molasses	6 tablespoonfuls
Juice of ½ orange or lemon	
Water	1 cupful (approximately)

The bran and paris green are mixed together dry; the molasses dissolved in the water; and the whole thoroughly mixed. The finished bait should be just moist enough to form a crumbly ball when squeezed in the hand. The bait should be scattered evenly and thinly on the soil around the plants in the evening on several nights in succession.

Young transplants can also be protected by forming a collar around each plant of a strip of tarred paper or cardboard pressed into the soil to hold it in place.

Snails and slugs

Delphiniums as well as many other plants are subject to attack by snails, especially by several shelless species commonly called slugs. These soft-bodied creatures frequent damp shady locations and are

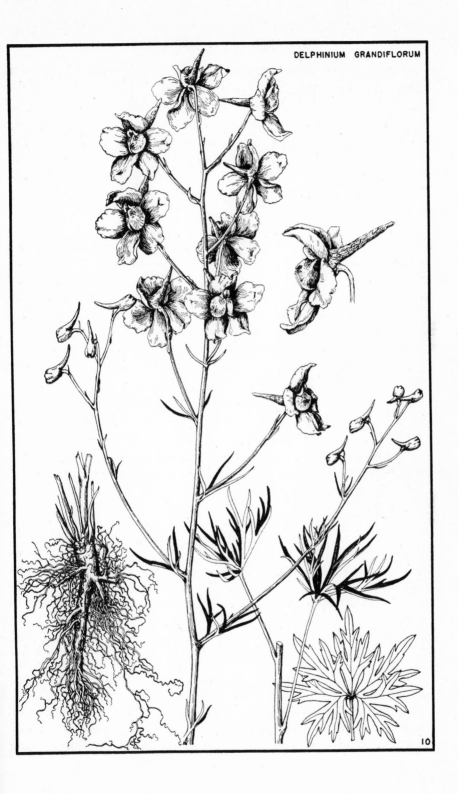

most active and injurious in cool rainy periods. They feed at night
and during the day remain hidden in the ground, under flats, pots, or
debris; and sometimes in cracks between the boarding of coldframes
or greenhouse benches. They eat ragged holes in leaves, gnaw stems
and also attack the underground parts. They leave a characteristic
trail of dried mucus secretion or "slime" wherever they go.

Control is by clean cultivation and sanitation, such as the removal
of plant debris and keeping the compost and manure piles some little
distance from the garden.

Until very recently control measures for snails and slugs have been
relatively unsatisfactory. Hand picking at night is very tedious, time-
consuming and limited. Poison baits containing arsenicals, including
commercial slug baits as well as home-mixed preparations, have not
been very effective. Irritant materials are of some value, particularly
copper-lime dusts and tobacco dust, but these must be applied liberally
and rather frequently to control slugs when they are abundant.

Fortunately, an amazingly effective slug bait has recently been
discovered, that offers a very satisfactory solution for the problem of
slug control. This bait has been extensively tested by the writer in
greenhouses, coldframes, and gardens and has proved uniformly
effective against the various common species of snails and slugs.
Usually a single application made at a time when slugs are active
will virtually eliminate them for a period of a month or longer. The
baits are very attractive to the slugs as well as quickly toxic to them.
The morning following an application the piles of bait will often be
found covered with dead slugs. The bait remains effective for a week
or more unless leached by heavy rains.

The bait consists of a mixture of powdered metaldehyde and bran.
Metaldehyde is apparently not manufactured in the United States at
present, but is made in France and Switzerland and sold in the form
of pressed tablets labelled "Meta" which are used as a fuel for small
camp stoves, chafing dishes, and so forth. The effectiveness of the
material as a slug poison was apparently discovered accidentally
through finding many dead slugs around pieces of "Meta" discarded
in parks. In 1938 several brands of metaldehyde slug baits have been
put on the market in the United States and Canada and are available
through seed stores and florist supply houses.

The metaldehyde slug bait is applied dry either broadcasted at
the rate of about 1 pound to 100 square feet or placed in small piles
about 3 feet apart.

Sowbugs

Sowbugs, also known as wood-lice and pillbugs, are sometimes injurious to delphiniums in coldframes or in damp shaded locations in gardens. They are oval rather flattened creatures, usually gray or grayish-brown in color, and curl up into a tight ball when disturbed. They are land-living crustaceans and thrive only in damp situations. Sowbugs live largely on decaying vegetable matter but when abundant sometimes cause noticeable injury to plants by gnawing stems and roots and eating out irregular holes in the foliage.

Control is by sanitary measures, such as the removal of decaying plant debris, manure and compost piles, and rotting boards from the vicinity of the garden.

Poison baits of several types have been effective. A good formula consists of 1 rounded tablespoonful of paris green thoroughly mixed with 2 quarts of bran. The materials are mixed dry and scattered evenly and lightly over the beds at the rate of 2 quarts to 100 square feet. The material should be kept off foliage as much as possible as it may cause burning.

Rocket Larkspur

PLATE 6. ENDPIECE

THE ROCKETS ARE ANNUALS of the simplest cultivation in any good garden. They are forms of what horticulturists know as *Delphinium Ajacis*.

This year I sowed named varieties in the open garden on the fifth of May and they began to show bloom late in July and were a glory in August. I sowed thickly in rows two feet apart, and thinned the plants as they developed to about five or six inches in the row. Results were all that could have been expected. The rows might have been as close as eighteen inches apart, but if the plants grow large they become rather crowded. My plants reached four feet in height and were well branched. They were thick with rockets of bloom. Ordinarily I leave a few plants for seed just for the interest of the many mature pods, but I do not save seeds for planting from such a mixed collection because they would probably be so crossed as not to come true to variety.

The plants I grew this year are all of one commercial race; thus I obtained a uniform size and character of plant with flowers, in the different varieties, white, blush, pink, deep pink or rose, carmine, lilac, blue, purple. All flowers are double but shapely and attractive. The spur is evident to one who wishes to look for it. In other years I have grown other races with equal satisfaction.

Although I grew the double-flowered form this year, I still like rows of singles, that show the larkspur form to perfection. The doubles, however, have interesting history. Basil Besler pictured several kinds of them in 1613. In fact, knowledge of this plant goes far back in history. The Latin poet Ovid knew it, or a similar species, by whom it was called hyacinth. Inside the hood of the single flower, formed by the two upper petals, are certain straight marks in dark color (barely suggested in Plate 6), supposed by the ancients to be AIA or a similar inscription, which were interpreted to signify Ajax, whence the genitive *Ajacis*, delphinium of Ajax.

In nature the Rocket larkspur is usually not a large or a vigorous plant. Often it runs only to a single stem, eighteen inches or even less tall. Sometimes it branches more or less throughout its length but it retains a strong central early-blooming leader that overtops the branches; this habit distinguishes it at once from the diffuse *D. Consolida* with which it is often confused.

In cultivation are dwarf Rockets, coming true to seed. They are compact leafy plants six to twelve or more inches tall, good for the near side of a parterre. They come in different colors, single and double. The dwarfs require the same culture as the tall or standard kinds.

Colors of the Rocket larkspur flowers are vivid, and commonly nearly or quite uniform in the same blossom. When the flowers begin to fall the garden ground is tinted as with flakes of tinted snow. Even on herbarium sheets many years old the colors may still be brilliant. The shape of sepals is also definite and attractive. The sharp flaring blades, together with the independent spur, make a joyful display in a good garden of Rockets.

The Rocket larkspur often escapes from gardens and may persist for some years about habitations. It is entered in North American manuals of botany as an introduced plant. This means that it sows itself from dropped seeds. Garden beds in which single forms have been grown are likely to raise a good supply the following year, and perhaps longer, without attention of the gardener. The self-sown stands are usually earlier blooming than planted rows, having had an earlier start. This year I noted them in bloom in North Carolina in early May and gradually later northward until early July in central New York.

With the Rocket larkspur we may associate *Delphinium orientale* inasmuch as the plants are much alike and cultural requirements are the same. This plant was not separated botanically from *D. Ajacis* until ninety years ago. Its special mark is the peculiar and persistent violet or violet-purple color of the flowers, a tint apparently not matched in the Rocket. The central leader of the plant is less pronounced and the pods are longer and usually thicker. It is little seen in cultivation, but it might add a pleasant variety to a garden of annuals.

Forking Larkspur

PLATE 8

THE FORKING LARKSPUR is the annual *Delphinium Consolida,* native in continental Europe and western Asia. It is a smaller plant than *D. Ajacis* and has not been so much ameliorated by cultivation; spurs very long and sharp; plant does not make a strong central axis or leader, but forks or branches about equally on all sides; leaves simpler, with long narrow acute and more erect divisions; seeds with separate rather than concentric scales.

Forking larkspur has a long history as a cultivated plant, and double-flowered races are mentioned and figured; the double and other horticultural kinds I have grown, however, turned out to be modified forms of what we know as *D. Ajacis* as revealed by the foliage and the seeds. Therefore, I do not place too much dependence on the literature.

We shall learn in the Enumeration that the genus Delphinium is not botanically one homogeneous group. It has been split into at least three genera. One of these genera is typified by *D. Consolida;* if we adopt this division then our plant becomes *Consolida regalis.* The substantive Consolida has been in use for centuries, even long before the advent of what we now know as systematic botany; it is related to the Latin participle *consolidare,* to make solid, in reference to supposed healing qualities; it was one of the consounds (healing plants) of medieval time, and *Consolida regalis* means the King's consound. When Linnæus made a binomial for the plant in the genus Delphinium he preserved the history with the name *D. Consolida,* putting the species name in apposition with a capital initial and not agreeing with the generic name in termination for gender.

All this discussion may not aid in growing the plant, nor should it hinder; and, for myself, I find satisfaction when I sow seeds of historic plants in feeling that I am kin of worthy souls of long ago; and I wonder how life seemed to them. The culture of this species is in all ways like that of the Rocket larkspur. One must expect less showy bloom, but should be interested in the bright flaring flowers on the ends of slender branchlets.

Other wide-branching small annual larkspurs to be associated with *D. Consolida* are *D. cardiopetalum*, *D. divaricatum*, *D. paniculatum*, which are more or less in cultivation. They require no special care.

The name *cardiopetalum* signifies the heart-shaped lower petals, and these petals are shown in the lower right of Plate 9. This plate was made directly from a living plant in 1938, and the artist has caught the spirit of the impertinent blue flowers that rear their tails to the sky.

Bouquet Larkspur

PLATE 10

THIS IS THE GROUP of *Delphinium grandiflorum*, known often to growers as *D. chinense* and *sinense*. It is a handsome and useful lot of free-blooming plants showy in the garden and adaptable to use in floral work. The sprays combine well with other flowers in bouquets. They are fine-leaved much-branched plants one and one-half to two feet high, from a hard tap-root.

There are good ranges in blues and blue-purple, mauve, reddish, to clear white. Flowers on my table from seeds sown this spring are one and one-half inches across, flaring and flat so that the color shows to advantage particularly as the bee is the same tint as the remainder of the blossom. The slightly hooked or straight spur stands straight back and is colored like the sepals. The wide-open flower, like a creature in flight, has probably given it the name Butterfly larkspur. It is also called Chinese larkspur.

Picture in Plate 10 was drawn in 1938 from plants reared from sowing in 1937. The plant came from a garden of showy Bouquet larkspurs of the same age and parentage, seeds purchased as *Delphinium chinense;* there was good demand for the large blue flowers in their open graceful racemes.

How long the Bouquet larkspur plant lives and freely blooms appears to depend much on conditions, but two or three years is perhaps the rule in New York and other northern parts. If you pull away the earth about the crown of new plants about the middle of September you will see the big white buds making ready for next year's stalks. In my own practice I expect two years of good bloom: sown in the open ground in early spring, bloom is obtained in August, September and October of that year; plants are not allowed to bear heavy crop of seeds, they are mulched in autumn, and the following year the bloom again is good, beginning usually in late June; then they are mostly displaced to make room for other tests. The plants are perennial. Roots can be purchased from dealers.

Bouquet larkspur appears to be a dominant type in hybridizing work. I see it coming up in characteristic form in rows of crosses between other species, often after several generations. It is variable under cultivation, not alone in color but in size of plant and in habit. There are dwarf varieties. Leaves also vary considerably in the depth to which they are cut and width of the divisions. The species is also variable in nature, as one would expect from its vast range in Siberia and China. Perhaps *D. tatsienense* is one of the extreme forms of it with relatively longer and curved spur, more diffuse or corymbose inflorescence, and perhaps a less wide-open flower and broader leaf-segments.

Double flowers are well known in *Delphinium grandiflorum*. As early as 1814 the following statement was published in England (in Botanical Magazine): "A double variety of this species is very common in our gardens, and much admired for the splendid blue colour of its flowers."

Garland Larkspur

PLATES 11, 12, 13

IF WE WISH A PUZZLE in names and origins we find it here. Whether we are now to deal with *Delphinium cheilanthum* or some other name, or with a half dozen names, we shall now attempt to determine, although the more technical part of the discussion is reserved for the Enumeration.

Perhaps the grower will say that I have begun discussions of these classes of larkspurs with Latin names and at least implied historical considerations, whereas he wants to know the plants. I reply that he cannot know the plants without knowing names. One cannot read much of the common writing on delphinium with any clear conception of the particular kind of plant the writer had in mind.

Delphiniums are not even divided into their natural groups or classes in the writings. In this book I have tried for the first time to define and explain such horticultural groups although I had made most of the names in my Manual of Cultivated Plants in 1924, but vernacular names cannot be exact and definite. Origins and relationships must be considered, and this requires technical names as definite as when a person is required to sign a legal document. If we are ever to know what we are doing in horticulture we must attempt to arrive at something like precision in the understanding of plants.

Yet I now accede to the reader long enough to define what I mean by the Garland larkspur, a title I first used in Hortus in 1930; and we shall at the same time learn how to grow the plants. The Garlands are perennial larkspurs of low stature or at least not tall and straight growth, leaves not cut into linear segments as in the Bouquet class, with blue flowers (and their derivatives) carried in open few-flowered racemes rather than in close long spikes such as are borne above the foliage by the Candle group, and a light colored bee. They bloom more or less continuously throughout the season. I cite Belladonna and Cliveden Beauty and what we call Formosum as examples of Garland larkspurs.

They are a showy and satisfactory lot, usually of long duration in

52

the garden as larkspurs go, perhaps four or five years or more if well treated. The sprays work well in bouquets and other decorations, imparting an informal touch. They are hardy and easy to grow, and usually carry only clear self colors; these colors range through the brilliant blues, and seedlings may come clear white; Moerheimii is a good white.

Here at my hand are blossoms of plants I grow as Cliveden Beauty, still moist from last night's rain. They are like the mazarine blue of the Ridgway chart, with faint suggestion of pink at the thickened tip of the sepals; there is purple tinge on the back, and particularly along the wrinkled long spur. The blossoms are one and three-fourths inches across; the spur is one inch long, with an empty collapsed end for perhaps nectar is not now secreted on the inner tube. Some of the flowers are horizontal, gazing steadily outward; others are a little declined, looking to the bright mulch of straw. The bee is large and nearly white, much lighter colored than the main part of the bloom; two upper petals are erect entire and stiff,—I can pull them out with their long spur-like nectaries; two lower petals are large and bulged, and they fill the mouth of the flower and each one bears a heavy beard of very light yellow; stamens and pistils are not visible but they appear when the lower petals are lifted,—twenty-three anthers I count now twisted down on their slender filaments with widely flattened base, and three pistils with stigmas dead after having received the pollen. From this plant Plate 11 is drawn as also Plate 12 showing the leaves just as they stand to the eye at their level except that the blade in the background at the bottom is flat as the botanist likes to see it for description; note the wide-flaring lower leaf cut to its base into rather narrow forked parts. The plants just outside my door are slender and lithe, swaying in the wind, thinly foliaged, thirty-four inches tall when straightened up; beside them is a clump of Candle larkspur, contrasting mightily with its big bunch of lower leaves and its stout stiff stems that stand like a captain on guard and now coming into its second bloom. The Cliveden Beauty is a bonny plant, graceful and cordial; it is one of the kinds I include in the class of Garland larkspurs; the plants began to bloom in June, and I shall have flowers to October. I purchased roots of this plant last year; I shall keep the plants until they give up.

Here also is Belladonna, standby of the Garlands, in good bloom August 15th from seeds I sowed on May 5th of this year; it also will bloom until cut by heavy frost. It is a coarser plant than Cliveden

Beauty with less narrowly cut leaves of a deeper darker green. It seeds very freely. The blossom is practically indistinguishable from that of the other. I know from former experience it will give us much satisfaction next year.

Now I look at Formosum, the plant known under that name in gardens, but it may not be *Delphinium formosum* of botanists,—the Latin word *formosum* means "beautiful" and perhaps it is not strange that a showy variety of cultivation should be given the name irrespective of its prior use in the genus. This Formosum of horticulture is much like Belladonna in foliage and flower color, but on strong central shoots the blossoms are likely to be in rather close and sometimes dense racemes after the manner of the Candles but the bee is that of the Garland set. The foliage is large and not so narrowly divided as in Cliveden Beauty. This plant I have raised from seeds with satisfaction; it blooms freely late in summer the first year and begins late in June or early July the second year.

The plant I grew nearly twenty years ago as *Delphinium Barlowii* was of the Belladonna kind, but plants now in my garden under that name are quite different; and both of them are wholly unlike the plant to which Barlow's name was originally applied, as we may learn from the Enumeration. My present *Barlowii* is apparently closely related to *D. grandiflorum* and may be a development from it; but the stock I formerly grew comes well within the definition of the Garland larkspurs.

Other horticultural varieties are Garlands, but perhaps these examples are sufficient to establish the group in the reader's mind. All are simple of cultivation, and we need not linger on that part of the subject. They are propagated by seeds; and probably established roots can be divided and I assume the plants can be increased by cuttings.

When we come to inquire about the species to which these plants belong we are against the most difficult botanical problem in the ameliorated delphiniums. It has been assumed they are derivatives of the Siberian *Delphinium cheilanthum*. The *formosum* of gardens is referred to *cheilanthum* as var. *formosum* by Huth. This species *D. cheilanthum* begins with Augustin Pyramus de Candolle in 1818, the name having been proposed, as he says, by Fischer in a letter. Yet it is strange that *cheilanthum* does not appear as a native plant in the great herbaria to which I have had access. Specimens cited by Huth mostly are plants considered by him to be botanical varieties of *D. cheilanthum*.

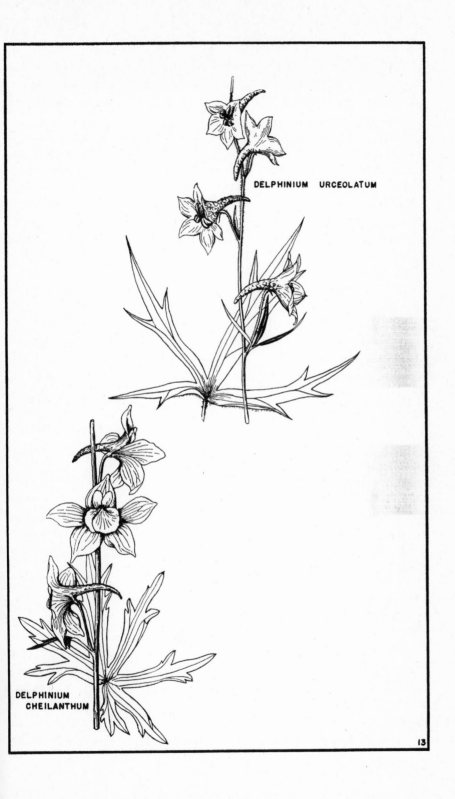

DELPHINIUM URCEOLATUM

DELPHINIUM
CHEILANTHUM

13

DeCandolle says it came from the region of Doroninsk in Dahuria, which is in Trans-Baikal Siberia near China. He says the flowers are size of those of *D. grandiflorum*, and I assume of the same color inasmuch as he does not mention that point; the two upper petals are as in *grandiflorum*, which would mean they are dark colored and not like many of the horticultural kinds we have supposed to be descended from this species.

A year later, 1819, Franz von Paula von Schrank published his folio on rare plants cultivated in the University gardens of Munich, Plantae Rariores Horti Academici Monacensis. He describes this plant in detail and figures it in color; the name he gives is *Delphinium cheilanthes* Fischer in letter, who got it in Dahuria. He says the flower is blue, the two upper petals violet-blue.

The dried plant Fischer sent to DeCandolle is preserved in his herbarium in Geneva, Switzerland, dated 1816. Photograph of this specimen is before me. Drawings on the sheet, apparently made by Fischer, bear the name *Delphinium cheilanthes*, as if he chose the spelling published by Schrank; inasmuch as it was first published *cheilanthum* by DeCandolle, however, that form of the name must hold.

It is a poor specimen, fragment bearing a few flowers and pods and upper leaves, but it appears to be the same plant as the plate in Schrank, who indicates it had been grown in Hortus Schwezing. The Fischer drawing shows a leaf and details of the dissected flower, all in agreement with Schrank.

Long before DeCandolle and Schrank there had appeared in two of the great works of Nicolaus Joseph Baron von Jacquin an account of a new species, *Delphinium urceolatum*. Brief description with a beautiful portrait appeared in his Icones Plantarum Rariorum in or about 1781, and a fuller description in his Collectanea 1786. These works were published in Vienna. From that day until this his *D. urceolatum* has remained a puzzle, sometimes referred as a synonym to *D. elatum*, sometimes taking the place of the name *exaltatum* of the tall species native in the eastern United States, sometimes disregarded.

Jacquin founded his species on a plant for many years in cultivation. He did not know its country. He described it as perennial, growing sometimes as high as five feet, hirsute toward base; leaves deeply five-palmately divided, standing in an urceolate (urn-shaped) or broadly bell-shaped form, the lobes acuminate and cut; flowers blue tinted dull red, in an erect simple raceme (portrait shows five flowers well separated from each other), the petals (sepals) all equal and acute; follicles 3, lightly villous. Portrait shows the bee as dark colored, the parts small and narrow.

Here now we have an old cultivated larkspur, properly named and described, at last to be accounted for. Is it the same species as *D. cheilanthum*? Are our present Garland larkspurs descended from them? There is no way of answering these questions by cytological or other microscopic studies. Accounts in usual horticultural literature are too general and inexact to be of much service. The inquiry must rest with the systematic botanist and he may only hazard an opinion. The solution must now await a thorough monographing of the genus, when the cultivated races are given coordinate attention with the natives.

Let us begin with the older species, *Delphinium urceolatum*. The available evidence is the original description and portrait. From the old picture we shall draw a leaf and two flowers, and put them in Plate 13. Note the relatively simple segments or divisions of the leaf and the very long points; also the rather small flowers with pointed sepals and dark center. I know of nothing like this now in cultivation. If any reader finds such a plant, let him send me a good piece of it to show the parts. Seventy-five years or more ago a plant was in cultivation in this country that appears to be the same as Jacquin's delphinium, although the flowers were more numerous in the raceme. It was called *D. delicatum* and *D. formosum* but was different from the *formosum* of the present day. Perhaps the flowers were not large enough to cause the plant to be preserved in gardens.

Jacquin pictures a pod and a seed of his plant. The seed is obovoid, without wings or surface marking, and is very different from that of the native *D. exaltatum* with which *D. urceolatum* was once identified. The leaves, flowers and inflorescence are also quite unlike, as one may see by comparing Plate 20.

It is singular that the name *urceolatum* has appeared so little in horticultural and botanical history. In 1816 in England a plate and description appeared under this name in Botanical Magazine. The plant was said to be perfectly hardy, and it was sent to the magazine "by John Walker, Esq. of Arno's Grove." The colored portrait is not much like the *urceolatum* of Jacquin's plate, although Huth cites it as if authentic. A paragraph in the account in Botanical Magazine itself suggests what I think is the probable relationship of the plate:

"We have no doubt but our species is the *urceolatum* of Jacquin, and sufficiently distinct from *exaltatum*, of which it has been supposed to be a variety. It seems to us to be more nearly allied to *Staphisagria;* and may be the long-spurred variety of that species mentioned by Willdenow."

When we come to *D. cheilanthum* we find better early evidences. I have a photograph, as I have stated, of Fischer's specimen and it is accompanied by small original drawings. Then there are three historic plates. First is the picture by Johann Georg Gmelin in the fourth volume of Flora Sibirica, 1769, which Fischer says (according to DeCandolle) is his *D. cheilanthum.* Second is Schrank's picture and full page description (in Latin and German) of *D. cheilanthes;* this account is cited also by DeCandolle in his Prodromus 1824. This picture is authentic, and from it I have taken parts for Plate 13. Third, I have the excellent account and colored plate in volume six of Botanical Register published in London in 1820. The plant was then "recently introduced and not mentioned in any record of our gardens." It is stated that "seed has been lately procured from the gardens at Moscow through the means of Dr. Fischer, and the plant raised in several of the nurseries about London." The portrait "was taken at Messrs. Colville's nursery in King's Road, Chelsea."

All these records show a plant bearing broader leaf-segments and different lobing from Jacquin's *urceolatum,* larger flowers with broad sepals and a light colored big bee with broad rounded lower petals. From these evidences I think it is specifically distinct from the Jacquin plant.

We may now examine descendants of this plant as shown in several early colored portraits. Three of these portraits and texts clearly show *D. cheilanthum* as it is displayed in the three historic plates we have just examined. They are: *D. formosum* in Die Gartenflora, Berlin, 1859, plate 253; *D. cheilanthum* var *Hendersoni* in Gardener's Magazine of Botany, London 1850; *D. cheilanthum* var. *Chauvieri* (var. *Hendersoni* of the British) in Lemaire's Le Jardin Fleuriste, Ghent 1851. The pictures all represent the plant I have called the Garland larkspur, to which group belong Belladonna, Bellamosum, most of Formosum, Cliveden Beauty, and a few others; all these garden races I shall place loosely under *Delphinium cheilanthum* until the problem is at last solved.

Many named garden varieties are in the Garland group of larkspurs, representing shades of blue, lilacs and darker colors, and whites. They may differ somewhat in foliage but come within defin-

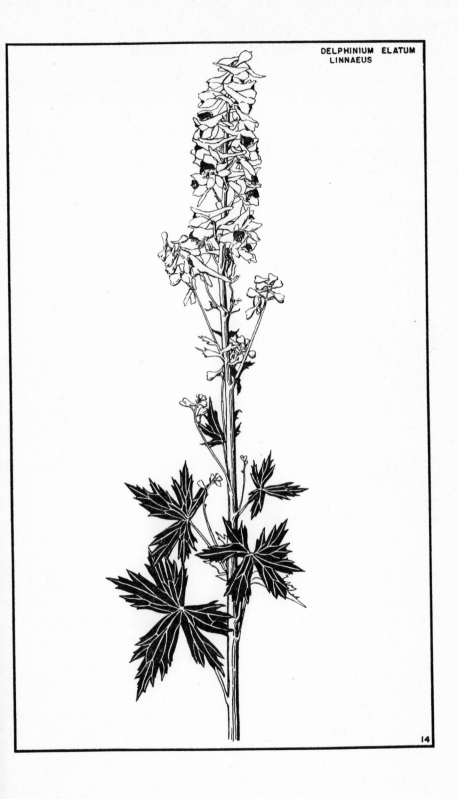

able limits. Varieties may be unlike also in size, habit, vigor, hardiness. They are sold as roots from nurseries and may come sufficiently true from seeds. These many varieties perhaps indicate a less mixedup parentage than in the Candle group and probably also a longer epoch of selection. They are likely to be continuous bloomers rather than croppers.

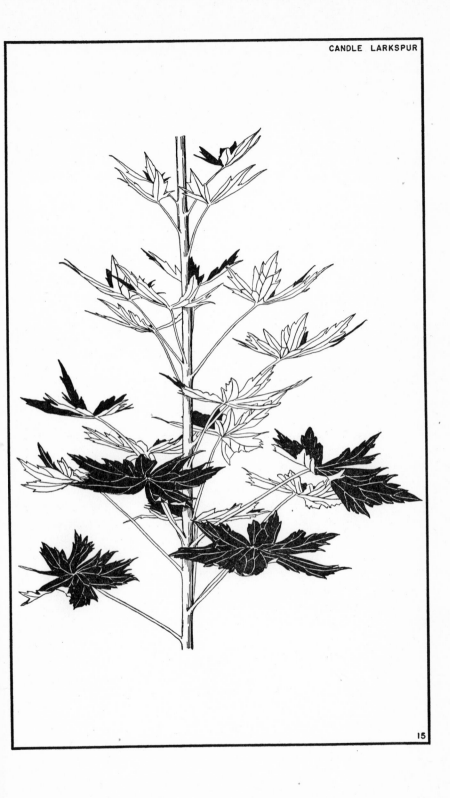

Candle Larkspur

WE ARE COME AT LAST to "the delphinium" of the delphinarians. These are amongst the most ornamental and desirable perennials in cultivation, known by the tall habit and the commonly dense terminal spike-like erect raceme that stands high above the clump of foliage after the first year; colors normally blue but now in many cyanic shades as a result of breeding, bee dark colored in the original or true types; they are croppers, producing quantities of bloom in June (in the northern states and Canada), and again in August or September or October particularly when the seeding stalks are early removed. Effective interest is now widespread in these plants, they are grown in great quantities, supplied by numerous nurserymen, bred into new and surprising strains by many persons. They constitute a modern and vigorous commitment in horticulture.

This great delphinium becomes a fancier's plant. Although in its less developed form it is essentially a denizen of yards and old gardens and a marker for division lines, yet the new and modified races appeal to devotees. The old delphinium is admired for its stately habit and pale blue flowers; the new delphinium stimulates excitement in novelties of form and color, and enthusiasts scan catalogues and periodicals for anything that promises to be different.

These differences lie in "constitution" of the plant, in the size and shape of the candle or spike, developed from the foot-long cluster of some years ago to those several feet long and five or six inches broad on stout stems that can carry the weight; in durability of the flowers so the lower blossoms in the spike will last till the upper ones are expanded; in position of flowers in the spike, at first a desire for a dense continuous candle as in Plate 17 but recently with flowers sufficiently separated to show individual shapes as in the frontispiece; in the size of the flower, from an inch across to two inches, and much more than that in special strains; in color from the old sky-blue to deep blues and purples and purple-reds, lavender, violet, clear white, and at present a flair for the pastel or soft light shades of the different colors;

in doubling of the flowers in differing grades, sometimes to the point of malformation. Yet the single and simple blues still hold interest in gardens of the people.

We need now to improve the single blues by selection and possibly by crossing, to the purpose that candles may be longer and of better form, if we can do so without lessening vigor of the plant or reducing its longevity. A planting of these delphiniums near my home is of plants ten or twelve years old. After the spring bloom the old stalks are removed, plants are thoroughly watered, fertilized if need be, and they are now vigorous in their second seasonal bloom. Some of the highly bred newer kinds become weak or perish after a year or two or three, and many growers are coming to the conviction that five years is sufficient longevity and are breeding to that end. My memory of the tall delphiniums of my early days is that we supposed them to live indefinitely, or at least, being uncritical, we did not think of any necessity to renew them. I certainly remember clumps of them persisting year after year, but of course I cannot affirm that renewal sometimes may not have been made by young plants arising from naturally dropped seeds. In a highly developed garden, particularly when there is a trained gardener, five years may be long enough for most perennials to live, the sense of persistence being satisfied by peonies and dictamnus and tansy; yet longevity is not a fault.

As for soil on which to grow Candle larkspurs I need not add to what I have said in the section on Cultivation of Delphiniums, and diseases and insects are handled by persons of special competence: see pages 25, 31. Advice to start only with strong young healthy stock can hardly be too often repeated. This is particularly true when one is growing for exhibition bloom, and when all chances of failure must be reduced to the minimum. Special attention must then be given to enrichment of the land and provision for supplying constant moisture, as well as protection from burning midday sun.

Exhibition of delphiniums is of two kinds,—an artistic display, a showing of different named kinds in competition for award or to meet a scale of points.

In the United States a great event in artistic display of delphinium was an exhibition in New York City in June, 1936, in the Museum of Modern Art by Edward Steichen, artist, delphinarian, President of the American Delphinium Society. Main part of the showing was in Candle larkspurs in great masses in large vases, of long well-filled spikes in many colors bred and grown by the exhibitor on his farm in

Connecticut; Garland larkspurs were also included. Striking portrayal of this exhibition is the double-page photograph in the Book of the American Delphinium Society for 1936. Reasons for Steichen's success in growing these great delphiniums are his artistic eye and a high ideal of perfection, discriminating choice of strong disease-free stock, good land well enriched, irrigation when necessary, rigorous elimination of all plants year by year that do not meet requirements, all coupled with accurate recognition of the special treatment required by the different strains or kinds. This exhibition demonstrated to the plant-loving public that delphiniums of major merit can be grown in the East as well as on the Pacific Coast and in Great Britain, an accomplishment well verified by many careful growers.

Competitive exhibitions naturally proceed on scales of points. The American Delphinium Society adopted a scale and it is published in the Book of the Society for 1933; this is the latest judging program, as I am informed by R. C. Allen, Cornell University, Secretary of the Society. It is here reproduced:

SCALE OF POINTS FOR JUDGING HYBRID DELPHINIUMS

Outlined by GERTRUDE W. PHILLIPS, revised by CHARLES F. BARBER, ALICE KAUSER, ALLAN G. LANGDON, LEON H. LEONIAN, and N. F. VANDERBILT

ENTRIES: Three classes of flower forms:
1. Singles: one row of sepals and at least five petals forming the eye.
2. Semi-double: two rows of sepals; eyes present or absent.
3. Double: more than two rows of sepals; eyes present or absent.

Thirteen color classes as follows:
1, 2, 3. Light, medium and dark blue; no trace of other colors.
4, 5, 6. Light, medium and dark mauve; no trace of other colors.
7, 8, 9. Light, medium, and dark purple; no trace of other colors.
10, 11, 12. Light, medium and dark bi-colors. Combinations or blends of blue, pink, mauve, purple and other colors, either on the same sepal, on different individual sepals in the same row, or when the outer row of sepals is blue and the inner some other color, are considered bi-colors.
13. Pure white, cream, or any other color or color combinations.

Four spike classes as follows:
1. Columnar or slightly tapering; massive.
2. Columnar or slightly tapering; slender and wiry.
3. Broad, conical.
4. Loose, open.

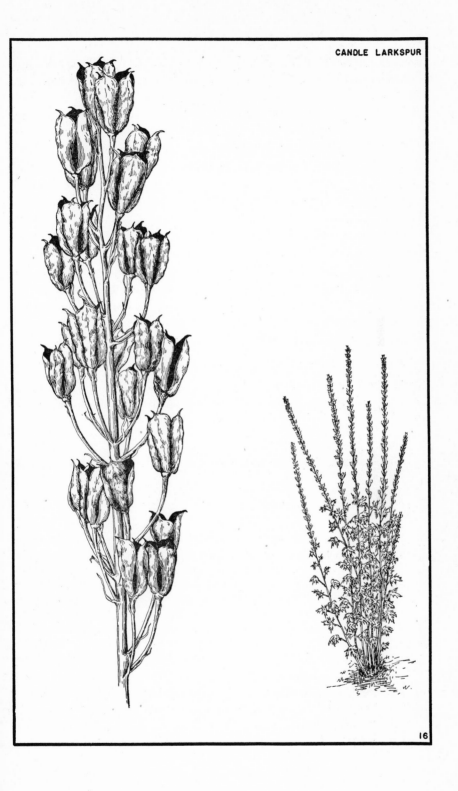

POINTS: Over 90 per cent should be considered approaching perfection; 85–90 per cent is very good, and 80 per cent satisfactory.

Color... 25

Flower spike

Length.. 10
Symmetry....................................... 10

Florets

Size... 10
Form.. 10
Placement....................................... 10
Substance....................................... 5

Foliage.. 10

Special features: Fragrance, new types of sepals and petals, new types of spikes, new colors, etc................ 10

Since foliage cannot be satisfactorily considered in indoor judging, the foregoing 10 points allotted to the foliage, may be used by the judge at his discretion.

Probably we have no true horticultural varieties in the Candle larkspurs, inasmuch as they do not come true to seeds. There are major races or strains, however, the result of selection and extra attention by expert growers, and each strain has characteristics of its own that show strongly in the seedling progeny even though the progeny may vary within itself. We have been familiar with important strains of producers in Great Britain and the continent of Europe, and now we have the benefit also of good races by breeders in North America. The names of these originators are well known to delphinarians and need not be repeated here.

Propagation is now to be considered, and we shall find a way to perpetuate particular plants that may not be expected to come true to seed. Most growers will purchase plants directly from dealers, but those striving for personal results may wish to grow their own stock. Advice in a book cannot make one expert in propagation of any plant, but it may set the inquirer on his way. Satisfactory results come from thoughtful practice, and aid should be sought of competent propagators.

I must add, before leaving this subject, that one should not buy delphinium plants (or seeds) because they are cheap. It costs time and much labor and patient oversight to raise stock that may be confidently expected to give good results in your garden. The extra you pay for such stock will be returned to you in satisfaction. You will not know the joy of delphinium culture until you have grown the best of the modern productions.

Ordinary seed propagation is simple in delphinium, except that certain species, as some of the native Americans, may not germinate the first year. All the annuals may be sown directly in the open garden as soon in spring as the ground is warm and dry, sometimes even before frost has ceased, with expectation of blooming plants in late summer (in the North) and autumn. If earlier bloom is desired, seeds may be sown in very early spring in flats or seed-beds under cover, the seedlings transplanted as needed. We have already learned that *D. Ajacis* does well from its seeds shed in autumn.

Usually I expect to obtain blooming plants in autumn from seeds of Garland and Candle larkspurs I have sown early in the open ground that year. Of course the bloom may not be characteristic of the plant and the plant itself will not be developed until the following year.

For large and commercial results, seeds are sown under glass, as in frames, and seedlings are pricked out into flats or seed-beds; and the work proceeds with expert precision, even as to the caution about soils and their treatment expressed by Leonian on page 25.

A particularly desirable perennial delphinium plant may be increased by division of the crown if it is still strong and active. The third year, or perhaps the fourth, the plant is dug up in early spring, washed clean, and then divided by cutting down through it with a sharp knife, as many parts being taken as there are strong buds (or shoots just starting) that can have good roots at the base. These parts are treated like seedling plants, handled with care, given good land and cultivation, not allowed to dry out; following year good bloom should result. The parts should be disinfected as divided. Few plants, perhaps four or five to twice that number, can be expected by division.

By cuttings the propagation of a good delphinium may proceed much faster, for as many new plants can be expected as there are crown-shoots produced on a plant chosen or grown for the purpose, and each cutting makes its own roots. Naturally, a very large strongly grown crown will give best results. The cuttings ordinarily root readily, but losses may arise in the growing process and particularly when the sand or soil has not been sterilized. Attention to all the requirements is essential, as ventilation of the frame or house, temperature, shade, watering, control of diseases and pests. The thoughtful grower will come through with good results, although one hundred per cent is not to be expected.

Cuttings are taken in early spring from strong crowns, when the shoots are three to five inches long; each one is cut with a heel at base, which is a part of the crown itself. After the cuttings are all removed the crown may be disinfected and planted out again for another crop the next season, if it is desired to save it.

The cuttings are inserted in disinfected sand, kept cool at the start (about 50° F.), moist, and most of the time from direct sun until they are rooted, which should be in three or four or even six weeks. When well rooted they are potted up in three- or four-inch pots containing sanded leaf-mold or similar material; from the pots they are turned out to the open ground, and should bloom the following year. There is a notion that varieties propagated by cuttings soon run out, but this is probably not the case when strong fresh stocks are used and the cuttings are capably grown.

Sometimes the crowns are lifted in autumn and are brought into heat in a greenhouse about January; growth fit for cuttings soon starts, and time may be gained in bringing the plants to bloom. Sometimes, also, cuttings are made from tip growths, but it is not the common method; nor would we expect to resort to layering to any extent in North America.

The novice at the growing of delphiniums of any kind should be willing to read attentively of the experiences of others in the books and magazines and reports. It will be a great help if meetings can be attended. The subject then begins to hold itself together and interest should continue year after year.

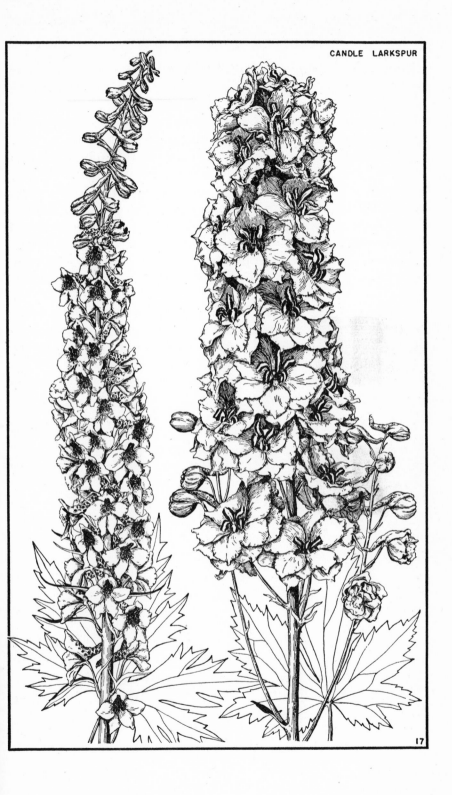

17

Red Larkspur

FROM THE EARLY DAYS of delphinium growing men have sought a red flower. The introduction of *Delphinium cardinale* from California marked an epoch to lovers of larkspurs. Thus Hooker wrote in England in 1855 when he founded the species: "Blue or purple or white *Larkspurs* are familiar to us in our gardens. We have now the pleasure of making known a species of *Delphinium* equalling if not surpassing any other in the size and symmetry of the plant, and excelling in the brilliancy of colour of the flower, and that as rich a scarlet as can well be looked upon."

In Belgium in 1856 *D. cardinale* was hailed with enthusiastic hope. Thus in Flore des Serres published in Ghent, in connection with a colored plate it was said: "This is a plant likely to make a sensation in the horticultural world. A scarlet larkspur! *Rara avis*, that is, the phoenix of the genus. Decidedly we need not despair of a blue rose." Louis Van Houtte declared that it might produce marvels by hybridization. The following year we find it in Boston, and statement in Magazine of Horticulture says: "It is a superb acquisition, and, aside from its own beauty, must be exceedingly valuable for hybridizing the other kinds, by which an infinite variety of colors may be produced."

Ever since the introduction of *Delphinium cardinale* and the earlier advent of *D. nudicaule* there has been expectation that from them a suitable red larkspur for general horticultural use would appear. Many attempts at modifying and crossing these species have been made in Europe and America. These attempts have failed of direct permanent results.

At present, however, we are in possession of a brilliant pink hardy perennial larkspur, of Dutch origin, that promises to be a real acquisition. It is the variety known as Pink Sensation, *D. Ruysii*, of which the American rights are in the hands of Jackson & Perkins, Newark, New York, who introduced it to the trade in 1938 and who propagate it by cuttings. I have observed this plant in quantity on their grounds and I make a formal diagnosis of it (Plate 18):

Pink Sensation.—Perennial, root fibrous; plant 2 feet and more tall, well foliaged, thinly glaucous, producing a strong central axis and many slender side branches; main stem nearly glabrous toward base but thinly hirsute above, the pedicels and outside of flower distinctly short-hirsute: leaves glabrous above but ciliate on margins and underneath on the ribs; blade primarily 3-parted and the lateral divisions again deeply lobed, glossy underneath, lower leaves with parts 1 inch broad and rather sharply lobed, upper leaves 3-parted and with narrow mostly not lobed divisions ½ inch or less broad: inflorescence 8–12 inches long, openly flowered and yet presenting a continuous mass of color, pedicels 1–1 ½ inches long and ascending, provided with a long slender undivided axillary bract and with a pair of smaller ones near the top; flower standing crosswise, light pink, approximately the thulite pink of the Ridgway color chart, 1 ¼–1 ½ inches long spur and all, greenish mark on each sepal; spur nearly or about ¾ inch long, straight except that the apex is curved downward, about equal to the sepals which are ovate and shortly acute, center of the sepals lighter in color; bee of 4 or 5 narrow glabrous separate petals, bifid and purple at the apex or the lower ones pink throughout, upper 2 petals prolonged into an included nectary; stamens conspicuous, more than 10: follicles 3, sometimes 4, becoming glabrous at maturity, curved and long-beaked, to ¾ inch long: blooms more or less continuously, beginning early in the season.

Pink Sensation is an airy plant in the disposition of its flowers, lacking the heavy effect of the Candle larkspurs. It is said to reach a height of five feet in Holland. It is stated to be mildew-free. It should make good bouquet material for informal work.

This larkspur, Pink Sensation, is supposed to be a hybrid between *Delphinium nudicaule* and an *elatum* variety. History of the initial experiments in the breeding of a red delphinium are given in Gardeners' Chronicle, London, August 29, 1931, by B. Ruys, proprietor of the Royal Moerheim Nurseries, Dedemsvaart, Holland. A similar account by Mr. Ruys appeared in the Book of the American Delphinium Society for 1933. Extracts are made from the Gardeners' Chronicle article:

"When I started the Moerheim Nurseries in 1888, hardy perennials were not nearly so popular as now, and if a catalogue of that time is perused (*e.g.* of Mr. Thomas S. Ware, Tottenham, England, who was one of the most prominent growers), it will be found that the collection of herbaceous plants was very poor compared with what we enjoy at the present time.

"This lack of variety was especially noticeable among Delphiniums, which were known only in shades of blue, purple and mauve, etc. The most celebrated raisers of new Delphiniums were Messrs. Lemoine, of Nancy, France, and Messrs. Kelway, of Langport, England. Quite a great sensation was created about that time, when Messrs. Kelway brought out a new colour by offering two new varieties, viz., Primrose, sulphur-yellow, and Beauty of Langport, cream-coloured.

"I always desired to raise new plants and the Larkspurs had a great attraction for me; indeed, my hope was to obtain a pure red and a pure white variety. With that purpose in view, I started crossing D. nudicaule with many other varieties and species, and by saving so much seed as I could from sulphur-yellow or cream-coloured varieties, I hoped to get a pure white form by repeated selection, but all my trouble, for years, was in vain.

"In the meantime, different firms offered new varieties as nearly white ones, which afterwards proved to be more or less cream-coloured, and they all had one great drawback, namely, a very poor constitution. At last, in 1906, I succeeded in getting a white form of the Belladonna type, which not only had pure white flowers, but also a very strong constitution. This new variety I called Moerheimi, and it was distributed in 1911. At present it is found in all parts of the world where Delphiniums are grown."

"My experiments with the purpose of getting a red Delphinium were not so successful. In 1902, I engaged a young lady who had made a special study of the hybridizing of plants, and she made as many crosses as possible with Delphinium nudicaule, but not a single seed was harvested, and after that I gave up this work for many years.

"In 1917, I engaged an assistant with university education, and we tried to cross D. nudicaule with D. elatum varieties, but again without any success. I despaired of success in obtaining the long-desired red Delphinium until, in the summer of 1929, in a batch of seedlings of D. nudicaule, quite accidentally, one plant was found with a stem four-and-a-half feet high, and when it flowered this proved to be in every respect an intermediate form between D. nudicaule and a D. elatum variety, not only in the colour of the flowers, but also in foliage and habit. Unfortunately, the colour was a dirty purple, and the plant had no decorative value, but now that we have many seedlings in two generations, there can be no doubt that this plant resulted from an accidental cross between D. nudicaule as the mother plant and a Delphinium elatum hybrid."

"In the spring of 1930, we had about two hundred seedlings, and nearly all of them started to flower in July and August of the same year, and four of them had flowers of a good red colour; one was a most brilliant red with flowers of good form and size, and growing three-and-a-half feet high. So at last my hope was fulfilled, and the long-wished for red Delphinium was raised.

"Last spring, every grain of seed was sown and of the plants raised from the best form—which we called no. 1—about twenty-five have pure red flowers, and these started to flower in the middle of July, and at present (August 11) they are still in full bloom (F_3 generation). The four red-flowered plants (F_2 generation) which flowered for the first time last year were transplanted last spring, as well as the original plant (F_1 generation), which was divided into four parts. This operation revealed roots intermediate in character between the two parents, as they were not so bulbous as in D. nudicaule and not so fibrous as in D. elatum, and, what is of great importance, all the plants are true perennials."

"So far, I have written only about the red plants of the F_1 and F_2 generations, but among the remaining seedlings we found several of great decorative value, ranging in colour from pink to dark violet, and some with a very conspicuous eye or 'bee'. Of course, all are being tested. The best forms will be propagated but it will be some years before they can be offered to the public."

For further history, see *Delphinium Ruysii* in the Enumeration, page 106. The variety Pink Sensation comes from a seedling that appeared in the Royal Moerheim Nurseries in 1933.

Key to Significant Species of Delphinium

Comprising those most likely to be met in gardens in North America or in literature of the subject. Most of the native American species are omitted inasmuch as they are little known in cultivation, and the entire group should be keyed together in a monographic study when specific lines shall be newly defined.

I. The annual larkspurs: leaves finely divided, into nearly or quite linear parts: seeds usually triangular in cross-section, the surface squamate or scaly.

    A. Petals (comprising the "bee") united into one body or part: follicle or pod solitary (one from each flower) unless sometimes in doubled flowers.

        B. Flowers in long simple racemes, the main stem constituting the entire height or continuing axis of the plant and the side branches (if any) plainly secondary: pod pubescent at maturity, usually three-fourths inch or more long.

            C. Blossoms in nature blue but running to other colors in cultivation although rarely if ever to real violet: strong plant with mostly closely packed often double flowers: spur long and slender, horizontal or upright . . . . *D. Ajacis*

            CC. Blossoms deep or intense violet: weaker plants for the most part, with single (not double) flowers: spur short, declined . . . . *D. orientale*

        BB. Flowers few on the ends of many forking branches, so that the plant has a diffuse open look rather than a long continuing axis: pod usually less than three-fourths inch long.

            C. Follicle (pod) glabrous.

                D. Blossom more than 1 inch across the face (unless in very dwarf forms); spur ¾ inch or more long, very slender: plant usually not exceeding 2 feet tall, forked . . . . *D. Consolida*

                DD. Blossom about ¾ inch across the face; spur less than ¾ inch long: plant usually 2–3 feet tall, paniculately branched . . . . . . *D. paniculatum*

            CC. Follicle pubescent (at least when young) . . . . *D. divaricatum*

    AA. Petals all free from each other, making 4 bodies or parts: follicles normally 3
    . . . . *D. cardiopetalum*

II. The perennial (or biennial) larkspurs: leaf-segments in most species ¼ inch or more broad: follicles in 3's or more; seeds usually (in ours) not squamate.

    A. Plant naturally biennial; stem more or less thick, soft and fleshy: flower open and flaring, with separated sepals; spur short in the cultivated kinds, at least not exceeding the sepals.

        B. Spur much shorter than the sepals . . . . *D. Staphisagria*

        BB. Spur about equalling the sepals . . . . *D. Requienii*

75

AA. Plant naturally truly perennial, although sometimes short-lived: flower usually not flaring so that the sepals stand flat open and separate; spur mostly equalling or exceeding the sepals: the common delphiniums of cultivation.

B. Color of flowers other than blue, purple, white.

Yellow...*D. Zalil*

(and var. of *nudicaule*)

Brown or brown-purple..*D. triste*

Bright pink...*D. Ruysii*

var. Pink Sensation

Red or orange-red: leaf-segments short, obtuse...............*D. nudicaule*

Scarlet: leaf-segments very long-acuminate..................*D. cardinale*

BB. Color blue, lilac, purple to white.

C. The small rock-garden species; alpines or of high mountains, a few inches to seldom 18 inches tall: flowers few to each stem.

D. Leaves geranium-like, margins toothed but seldom lobed..*D. cashmirianum*

DD. Leaves deeply lobed or cut.

E. Herbage or stems sticky-pubescent to tomentose.......*D. Brunonianum*

EE. Herbage or stems silky.............................*D. Pylzowii*

EEE. Herbage or stems glabrous or essentially so.

F. Ultimate lobes of leaf pointed....................*D. likiangense*

FF. Ultimate lobes obtuse..........................*D. Przewalskii*

CC. The general garden species, tall erect usually leafy-stemmed plants: flowers abundantly produced.

D. Inflorescence a long spike-like raceme that stands well above the basal foliage when the plant is mature, the many flowers being arranged along a main continuing central stem or axis.

E. Leaves cut into many linear parts......................*D. fissum*

EE. Leaves cut into parts ¼ inch or more broad.

F. Stem and foliage prominently hirsute...............*D. vestitum*

FF. Stem and herbage glabrous or only pubescent.

G. Ultimate leaf-divisions acute or acuminate.

H. Upper petals dark purple.....................*D. elatum*

HH. Upper petals brownish...................*D. Duhmbergii*

HHH. Upper petals same color as sepals, blue-purple..*D. exaltatum*

GG. Ultimate leaf-divisions obtuse................*D. Maackianum*

DD. Inflorescence in short or open racemes, not spiciform or candle-like on a central axis.

E. Leaves cut into many parts, most of which are ¼ inch or less broad, at least those on stem.

    F. Spur straight, or not curved....................*D. grandiflorum*

    FF. Spur hooked or decidedly bent at end.............*D. tatsienense*

EE. Leaves with broader segments or main divisions, most of them ½ inch or more wide at middle.

    F. Spur large, very obtuse, standing straight up.......*D. macrocentron*

    FF. Spur upright, nearly 2 inches long, more or less obtuse..*D. Wellbyi*

    FFF. Spur horizontal or oblique in position, pointed, usually less than 1½ inches long.

        G. Stems very leafy and covered, less than 2 feet tall..*D. oxysepalum*

        GG. Stems leafy in the ordinary way, usually taller.

            H. Bee not darker in color than sepals, usually lighter.

                I. Follicles strongly reticulate or netted......*D. dictyocarpum*

                II. Follicles not netted.....................*D. cheilanthum*

            HH. Bee prominently darker than the sepals.

                I. Leaf-points very long-acuminate..........*D. urceolatum*

                II. Leaf-points not so......................*D. yunnanense*

Enumeration of Delphinium

Species cultivated in North America

HERE ARE ENTERED the one hundred and ten binomials known to me in the North American trade or in our literature of cultivated things. They reduce themselves, for our purposes, to seventy-six species and horticultural units; that is, about one-third the names are synonyms of one grade or another.

This leads me to explain why names become synonyms, for I find there is confusion about it in minds of many persons. Names are not made to be synonyms or duplicates. They fall into synonymy in the course of events. Two reasons may be noted. (1) A botanist describes what he considers to be a new species in nature; it turns out, as the subject is developed, to be only a variant of another species previously described and the name becomes a synonym of the older name. Sometimes the proposed new species presents minor differences from the accepted species and it may be regarded as a variety. Synonyms seldom represent exact duplication. (2) A horticulturist finds something new on his grounds or produces it by selection or crossing; he gives it a Latin name without knowing that another plant in the genus already bears the same name; his name falls and he is under obligation to find another name for it if it deserves a name. Usually, however, he makes a binomial for something that is only a form or minor variant of a regular species, and his name falls into synonymy under that species. The following pages carry many horticultural synonyms, as *atropurpureum, candelabrum, caucasicum, formosum, hybridum, laxiflorum, pumilum, sinense, sulphureum, truncatum.*

This Enumeration is not a monograph or a botanical treatise. It endeavors to account for horticultural things but the language must be in botanical terms to make it mean anything in identification. The standing of the different names, as to category and synonymy, follows what appears to be acceptable current practice. The American species are yet imperfectly understood, and they need critical revision; such revision would probably change our nomenclature radically in some cases, but this is not to be deplored inasmuch as nomenclature in plants, as in chemistry or merchandizing, represents the state of knowledge of its time. If botanical nomenclature remains forever the same then knowledge and opinion are also stationary.

There is naturally no effort here to admit all native delphiniums. Such an enlargement would be confusing as well as quite outside the purpose of the book. If additional species are introduced to cultivation, the delphinarian should be able to keep track of them, or perhaps they will be recorded by the American Delphinium Society. They will appear in the ten-year issues of Hortus and its five-year supplements.

Not all the delphiniums in this Enumeration may be in cultivation with us at any moment, and I do not undertake to say where they may be obtained. Like fond memories, they come and go.

The genus Delphinium as now generally accepted is not homogeneous. At different times it has been split into separate genera, as Consolida, Delphinastrum, Staphysagria, and others. On the other hand, it has been enlarged to include Aconitum. Any gardener will recognize the great similarity between the larkspurs and aconites in foliage and in seed-pods. Structurally the aconites differ in the nature of the upper sepal which is developed into a hood rather than a spur. In pre-Linnæan times the use of the two names was not separated as carefully as now. In some kinds of aconites the hood is not very clearly formed. Huth presents Delphinium with two subgenera: Consolida, with normally a solitary follicle and petals united into one body or organ; Eudelphinium, with three or more follicles and the four petals separate.

In 1914 Dr. J. A. Nieuwland in the American Midland Naturalist recognized Consolida as a genus and placed our occidental species in Delphinastrum, transferring the specific appellations to that generic name.

In the present book we hold to the customary interpretation of the genus Delphinium.

Unless otherwise stated, the species in this Enumeration are perennial.

DELPHINIUM. Herbs, annual, biennial, perennial, root fibrous, woody, tuberous, stem erect or ascending, glabrous, pubescent, hirsute, tomentose: leaves all radical, or alternate and mostly cauline, broad, palmately cut, lobed, or dissected, long-stalked and petiole often dilated at base or the cauline ones sessile, blades becoming simpler toward top of stem and finally passing into trifid or simple

bracts in the inflorescence which is racemose on end of main axis or
on branches and sometimes so dense as to appear spicate (spiciform)
or flowers seldom all solitary on scape-like stems: flower hermaphro-
dite, common ones proterandrous, strongly irregular; calyx large and
colored and showy as if a corolla, sepals 5 and separate, the upper
one prolonged into a prominent spur, the blades ovate or broader and
commonly acute or at least narrowing to apex; petals 4, short and
compacted into the center of the flower (forming the "bee"), either all
separate or combined by their claws into a single structure, upper
pair erect and blades usually narrow, the two producing a long single
or double spur (nectary) that projects into the outer sepal spur, lower
pair variously deflected and mostly expanded and closing the throat,
usually bearing conspicuous stiffish hairs of a different color (beard);
stamens 10 or more, mostly covered under the lower petals; pistils
1–5, more or less hidden behind the stamens: fruit follicular, mostly
1 or 3 follicles maturing, containing many superimposed seeds which
are angled or flattened, sometimes winged, often cross-ribbed or
bearing separate or concentric scales (squamate).—*Delphinium*,
Linnæus 1753.

Ajacis. ROCKET LARKSPUR. Plate 6. Erect annual with forking
or fibrous root, stem and herbage finely pubescent to glabrous,
sending up a direct central axis 1–5 feet tall and bearing several to
many slender ascending laterals, all stems floriferous: foliage very
finely divided, at frequent intervals along the stems, consisting of
primarily 3-parted leaves on very short expanded petioles but the
upper ones sessile, each part (in the main leaves) again twice or
thrice divided, the ultimate obtusish parts or lobes 1/16–1/8 inch or
more broad, the central primary division long-stalked: flowers
originally blue or purplish, ¾–1 inch across in nature, an inch apart
more or less, along the main and lateral axes, making at expansion
continuous rods of bloom 3–12 inches long; pedicels 1 inch or less
long, carrying a pair of short bracts above the middle and standing
in the axil of a reduced leaf or leaf-bract; sepals ovate and more or
less acute, exceeded by the sharp horizontal or flaring or upright spur;
petals cohering into a single body open through its center up and
down, 2-lobed at apex and somewhat bulging at base: follicle 1 from
each flower (unless from double garden kinds when there may be 2
or 3), nearly cylindrical and with a tapering oblique apex, somewhat
turgid, to ¾ inch long, finely pubescent; seeds at maturity exceeding
1/16 inch in length, dark brown, strongly angled, corrugated or
plaited crosswise all over.—*D. Ajacis*, Linnæus 1753; *D. Gayanum*,
Wilmott 1924.

Mediterranean region, as southern Europe and northern Africa;
spontaneous or naturalized elsewhere. In North America it has wide
range as an introduced run-wild plant. In Europe are a few natural
varieties but they appear not to have come into cultivation. As a
garden plant it appears in many full-double forms, in different

statures, and in many colors and shades except the xanthic or yellow series.

Linnæus did not know the habitat of the plant he described a *Delphinium Ajacis.* His specimens, preserved in the Linnean Society of London, are three small plants that rest on an herbarium sheet, al double-flowered.

The Linnæan record on this species is not clear. He apparently included in it the plant now separated as *D. orientale.* Wilmott hold that the plant meant by Linnæus as *D. Ajacis* is in reality *D. orientale* described by Gay in 1848; that is, *D. orientale,* Gay, becomes *D. Ajacis,* Linn. For the other plant commonly called *D. Ajacis* he proposes the name *D. Gayanum,* "a most unfortunate change which will cause trouble but cannot be avoided as the evidence is unshakable." (A. J. Wilmott, Journal of Botany, lxii, p. 26, 1924). Nomenclature in the Ajacis group is under investigation abroad as this book is released to the press, and therefore the customary treatment is retained here.

albescens: *D. virescens.*

alpinum: *D. elatum* var. *alpinum.*

amœnum of gardens is one of the *elatum* group.

Andersonii. Low from a thickened root, 2 feet or less tall, not very leafy, glabrous or very nearly so, producing several stems, somewhat glaucous: leaves slightly hairy, 1–about 3 inches broad, deeply cleft into very narrow parts that are linear or oblong, teeth obtuse to acutish: flowers deep blue in open racemes 10 inches or less long, pedicels 1 inch more or less; spur short, curved at tip, usually shorter than the sepals which reach ½ inch long: follicles 3, nearly glabrous, about ½ inch long including the slender beak; seeds not squamate.— *D. Andersonii,* Gray 1887; *D. tricorne* var. *Andersonii,* Huth 1892; *D. Leonardii,* Rydberg 1912; early collected by C. L. Anderson.

Foothills and canyons, on eastern side of northern Sierras in California; also western Nevada and Utah.

arizonicum: listed name.

atropurpureum: garden name for a dark purple strain of the *elatum* group.

azureum: *D. carolinianum;* the name *azureum* is sometimes employed, however, for azure strains of Bouquet and Garland and Candle delphiniums.

Barbeyi. Leafy lightly pubescent plant, little if at all branched, to 3 feet or more: breadth of leaf-blades equalling or exceeding the length, the general outline reniform or cordate-orbicular, 3–4 inches across; main divisions 3 and these again divided or acutely lobed: inflorescence a short spiciform raceme with foliage to its base, the hairy-pubescent pedicels scarcely bracteate at apex; flowers deep blue, to 1½ inches long, standing crosswise or horizontal; spur ir-

regularly but not markedly curved, wide at its base; sepals broad, attenuate or even caudate, somewhat pubescent; bee lighter colored, the upper petals whitish but blue-tipped, lower ones blue and bearded: follicles 3, glabrous.—*D. Barbeyi*, Huth 1893; *D. exaltatum* var. *Barbeyi*, Huth 1892; dedicated to William Barbey.

Mountains to at least 11,000 feet, in Colorado, Utah, Wyoming, in spruce and alpine areas.

Barlowii. In describing this "garden variety" John Lindley in 1837 said it was "the most gorgeous mass of deep lapis-lazuli" with which he was acquainted in the vegetable kingdom. The plant pictured in Botanical Register (t. 1944), London, was in the "rich collection of hardy herbaceous plants in the nursery of Messrs. Rollissons of Tooting." The nurserymen said they received the plant from Manchester several years previously under the name *Delphinium Barlowii*, "and we believe it to have been raised by a florist of that name. . . .; undoubtedly it is an hybrid production, and we think the parents to be Delphinium grandiflorum and Delphinium elatum."

The Lindley colored plate shows foliage of the *elatum* kind, densely doubled button-like blue flowers with strong purplish over-color, and a very short curled spur such as I have not known in any cultivated larkspur, unless in the Staphisagria group. All the stock I have seen in cultivation as *D. Barlowii*, over a number of years, is very different from the Lindley plate and is not all the same thing; probably this old delphinium is not now known.

Most of the contemporaneous *D. Barlowii* is one of the forms or derivatives of *D. cheilanthum*, probably best referred to the var. *formosum*. The plant I have grown as *D. Barlowii* over a period of fifteen years, is deep rich blue with purple tint, sepals somewhat lighter in the center inside, bee white but with blue-purple margins, beard lightest yellow. It is nothing like the Lindley original.

Belladonna: see *D. cheilanthum* var. *formosum*.

Bellamosum. A horticultural race to be associated with the *D. cheilanthum* group (var. *formosum*). It is still in the trade, but supposed to have a weaker constitution than Belladonna and apparently not now employed as a stock by breeders. It bears deep blue flowers, in that respect differing from the light or azure blue of *Belladonna*.

bicolor. Slender, 6–20 inches high, with a thick or fascicled but not tuberous root system; stem glabrous to lightly glandular-pubescent, few-leaved, the petioles much exceeding the blades which are 1–3 inches across and circular to reniform in outline but divided to base into three parts which are again forked or divided into nearly or quite linear obtuse lobes: flowers purple-blue to lavender-blue, nearly or quite glabrous, 1-1 ½ inches long over all, in an open raceme of a dozen or fewer blossoms, the lower pedicels 1 inch long and bracted at the top; spur straight to lightly curved, usually exceeding the sepals and often lighter colored than they; bee prominent, the upper petals brownish-yellow and veined, lower petals purple and bearded: follicles 3, about ¾ inch or less long, beaked, glabrous to viscid-pubescent; seeds oblong, ridged, not squamate.—*D. bicolor*, Nuttall 1834; *D. glareosum*, Greene 1898.

Dry lands in mountains, alpine slopes, South Dakota to Utah, Saskatchewan and Washington and Oregon; a choice dwarf for rock-gardens.

Brownii. Leafy-stemmed plant to 3 feet tall, axis glabrous: leaves cleft into about 5 divisions, somewhat puberulent, the parts once or twice divided into narrow acute lobes: inflorescence a lax raceme, with slender curved and twisted pedicels less than 1 inch long; flowers dark blue or purple; spur straight, short and thickish, less than ½ inch long; sepals ½ inch or less long, obtuse or acutish; petals blue or purplish, tinged yellowish, with yellow beard: follicles 3, glabrous.—*D. Brownii*, Rydberg 1902; type collected at Banff, Alberta, by Stewardson Brown.

Meadows, Montana to Alaska. Perhaps a form of *D. scopulorum*.

Brunonianum. Dwarf leafy plant with musky odor in its native place, 1 foot tall less or more, the simple or branched stem somewhat sticky-pubescent to tomentose: leaves geranium-like, on long petioles sheathing at base; blade pubescent, reniform, 3-4 inches long and the breadth greater, parted to half or more their depth into 3 or 5 broad incised lobes: flowers large, pale blue with purple stripes toward the margins, horizontal or somewhat declined on long bracted pedicels; spur nearly straight, thick as it joins the sepals and about one-half their length, the sepals very broad and about 1 inch long; petals dark purple, the lower ones orange-bearded: follicles 3 or 5, villous, less than ½ inch long, flattened; seeds not squamate.—*D. Brunonianum*, Royle 1839; named after "the distinguished Mr. Brown" who put collections at Royle's disposal.

High mountains, Tibet; some of its forms in Afghanistan and Turkestan. Rock-garden subject. A plant once grown in this country as *D. Brunonianum* belongs with the *urceolatum* group.

Bulleyanum. To 3 or 4 feet and more tall, leafy-stemmed, axis glabrous except in the inflorescence and somewhat glaucous or violet: leaf-blade broader than long, 3-4 inches across the longest way, sparingly pilose, deeply parted into 3 main divaricate divisions and these again lobed and notched into acute points: inflorescence of loose open more or less panicled racemes, the pubescent narrow-bracted pedicels 1 inch long more or less and ascending; flowers deep blue, pubescent, 1 inch or less long, standing crosswise or nearly so; spur (a characteristic feature) doubled back on itself forming a complete loop; sepals long-ovate and bluntly acute; petals shorter than sepals, blue, the lower ones barbed: follicles 3, sparingly pilose.—*D. Bulleyanum*, Forrest 1912; bears the name of A. K. Bulley, English nurseryman.

Lichiang Mountains, Yunnan province, western China. Known by its spreading leaf-divisions and hooked spur.

californicum. Tall leafy pubescent larkspur, to 6 or 7 feet, from a fascicle of thick roots, little branched, the stem only lightly pubescent toward base: leaves large, blade and petiole pubescent, 3–6 inches across, divided beyond the middle into 3 main parts of which the lateral parts are again divided, the lobes or segments acute or acuminate: inflorescence densely spiciform, to 1 ½ feet long, hairy-pubescent lower pedicels 1 inch or so long and upper ones shorter and all ascending and usually bracted near the center or above; flowers conspicuously hairy-pubescent, white or whitish outside, ¾ inch or less long, not opening fully; spur straight, exceeding or equalling the broad scarcely acute sepals; petals often purplish, bearded: follicles 3, nearly or quite glabrous, beaked, less than ½ inch long; seeds wrinkled —*D. californicum*, Torrey & Gray 1838.

Western central California, on low hills near coast and on slopes of Coast Range.

candelabrum: old name for the rocket form of *D. Ajacis*.

cardinale. SCARLET LARKSPUR. Plate 22. Tall branchy perennial with shining stems that are nearly or quite glabrous, bearing few large leaves and becoming nude in fruit, to 6 or 8 feet; roots branching and woody: leaves various in size and appearance, practically glabrous, mostly radical; basal ones very long-stalked and blades to 10 inches across, divided practically to base into 5 or 7 long narrow divaricate acuminate parts that may be again sharply lobed; stem-leaves few, similar in division but smaller and the lobes linear to filiform: inflorescence of panicled very open racemes of which the central one may be 1 ½ feet long, the ascending bracted pedicels to 2 inches long and sometimes more than one from an axil; flowers bright scarlet with yellow center (bee), 1 ½ to nearly 2 inches long, standing well asunder in an ascending or somewhat declined position or sometimes the terminal ones close together; spur ¾–1 inch long, nearly straight, exceeding the broad blunt sepals; petals yellow, the upper with unequal lobes, lower ones ovate and hairy: follicles 3, standing stiffly erect on their pedicels at maturity, about ½ inch long and slender-beaked, thick, glabrous, much-veined; seeds sharp-angled or narrowly winged, not squamate.—*D. cardinale*, W. J. Hooker 1855.

Southern California among bushes and trees at lower elevations; Lower California, Mexico. A showy and striking plant in bloom, often requiring staking in cultivation; not hardy in the northeastern states; sometimes taken up in autumn and stored until spring. In a greenhouse I have seen it trained 12 feet high. When Hooker described the plant and founded the species in Botanical Magazine, London, he wrote: "We have now the pleasure of making known a species of Delphinium equalling if not surpassing any other in the size and symmetry of the plant, and excelling in the brilliancy of colour of the flower, and that as rich a scarlet as can well be looked upon. It is one of the many novelties detected by Mr. Wm. Lobb in California, and introduced to our gardens by Messrs. Veitch and Sons, of the Exeter and Chelsea Exotic Nurseries. Treated as a hardy annual, it cannot fail to be a great favorite with all lovers of handsome flowers." He states that the cultivated specimens in England were 2 to 3 feet high.

cardiopetalum. Plate 9. Low annual 10–20 inches tall, forking, axis finely pubescent: leaves 1–2 inches across, cut to base into several or many very narrow or linear acute divisions: inflorescence of several erect spike-like racemes 2–5 inches long, the short erect pedicels bracted toward the top; flowers blue, about ¾ inch long, standing crosswise; spur upturned, acute, longer than the narrow mostly blunt sepals; petals blue, not barbed, blade of the lower ones cordate: follicles 3, glabrous for the most part, about ⅜ inch long, freely produced; seeds nearly globose, bearing transverse plates.—*D. cardiopetalum*, DeCandolle 1818; *D. halteratum* var. *cardiopetalum*, Huth 1895.

Fields, southern France. An interesting short-season flower-garden annual, of the simplest culture.

carolinianum. Pubescent, rising 1–2 feet from a short clustered thick prongy root, mostly nearly or quite simple, main leaves at the base: leaves cut into linear or narrow-oblong segments that are again divided or lobed, ultimate parts sharp-acute, lower ones 2–3 inches across, cauline ones smaller and simpler and passing into linear bracts: inflorescence a long terminal open raceme, pedicels pubescent and erect; flowers blue, lightly pubescent, 1 inch long more or less, standing crosswise; spur straight except at bent tip, equalling or exceeding the nearly or quite obtuse sepals; petals colored like sepals on the end, lower ones bearded: follicles 3, pubescent, about ½ inch long; seeds somewhat winged, rugose.—*D. carolinianum*, Walter 1788; *D. azureum*, Michaux 1803.

Open and grassy places, Georgia to Texas and Arkansas. Plants in cultivation as *D. carolinianum* are likely to belong to the *D. cheilanthum* group.

var. **Nortonianum.** Large plant, 3–4 feet tall, more pubescent, leaves larger with longer lobes: flowers deep bluish-purple, with ascending spur: follicles ¾ inch long with diverging tips; seeds strongly winged, very rugose.—*D. carolinianum* var. *Nortonianum*, Perry 1937; *D. Nortonianum*, Mackenzie & Bush 1902; *D. azureum* var. *Nortonianum*, Palmer & Steyermark 1902; dedicated to J. B. S. Norton, American botanist.

Ozark region, Missouri.

cashmerianum. Low perennial with weak or flexuose stem to 1½ feet high but usually less, simple or forked, glabrous or pubescent: leaves mostly radical and long-petioled like those of a geranium, orbicular or broad-ovate in outline, 2–4 inches across, sometimes scarcely lobed although the margins strongly toothed, but mostly 5–7-lobed about to the middle and again cut-toothed: inflorescence corymb-like of 10 or 12 or fewer large flowers which are horizontal or declined, the short pedicels hairy-pubescent and prominently bracted; flowers about 2 inches long, truncate at base below the spur, azure-blue, pubescent, the sepals broad and obtuse and not expanding widely; spur broad, somewhat curved, obtuse, much shorter than the sepals; upper petals black-purple, the others greenish and barbed: follicles 3, hirsute.—*D. cashmerianum*, Royle 1839.

Himalayas, to 15,000 feet; a rock-garden subject in cultivation; not often seen in North America.

caucasicum of botanists is referred to *D. speciosum;* that of cultivation is apparently usually *D. elatum;* the name has also been applied to *D. grandiflorum.*

cheilanthum. Garland Larkspur. Plate 13. Racemose open-flowered tall perennial with simple or branched stem to 3 feet tall, herbage pubescent or glabrous: leaves palmate, 5-parted to the base except the upper ones which are 3-parted, petioles nearly or quite as long as the blade, main divisions narrow-cuneate to narrow-oblong, ½ inch or less broad, lengthwise about 3-ribbed, each narrowly and acutely trifid or lobed toward the end: inflorescence of relatively short and open 2–6-flowered racemes, not spiciform, peduncles with parted bracts at base and pedicels with simple bracts; flowers deep blue to whitish, large, on long pedicels and mostly somewhat declined, sepals thinly pubescent outside, blunt; spur about equalling the sepals and straight or somewhat curved at end; upper petals pale yellow or blue and glabrous, lower petals large and ovate to roundish and barbed, making a big bee filling throat of the flower: follicles 3, pubescent or glabrous, to 1 inch long and apex curved; seeds 3-angled and wing-margined, not squamate.—*D. cheilanthum*, Fischer ex De Candolle 1818; *D. cheilanthes*, Fischer ex Schrank 1819.

Siberia, China. Probable original of the Garland larkspurs; see page 54.

var. **formosum.** Plates 11, 12. Flowers large, 1 ½–2 inches across, with bold mostly blunt sepals, rich blue; petals all yellowish and conspicuous, the upper ones somewhat hooded or bent over, the lower ones prominently orange-bearded; spur straight, often more than 1 inch long: follicles pubescent, broad; seeds wrinkled, not squamate, narrowly winged: leaves usually with long large ultimate lobes.— *D. cheilanthum* var. *formosum*, Huth 1895; *D. formosum* of gardens but not of botanical literature.

A conspicuous larkspur because of its large blue flowers with yellow-and-orange bearded bee and prominent spur. The leaves are variable in shape and subdivision. It undoubtedly covers races of different garden origin. Forty-seven years ago I grew this plant under the name *chinense*, showing how old are the confusions in the larkspurs.

Belladonna larkspur, now deservedly popular, is to be associated systematically with var. *formosum* although differing in some respects and distinguished by growers. It is a free-growing delphinium of the branching type, blooming over a long season, with large flowers in turquoise-blue although deep rich blues, practically blue-purples, may appear in a batch of seedlings. The bee is practically white except the beard, which is faint light yellow. Leaves are of the Cheilanthum kind, deeply 3-parted and strongly ribbed, the parts again divided or lobed.

The variety Belladonna began to receive attention in England about 1880, supposed to be a garden hybrid of unknown parentage.

Consolida. FORKING LARKSPUR. Plate 8. Annual, 5–20 inches tall, leafy, stem prominently forking and closely pubescent or glabrous: leaves small and divided into linear lobes, 2 inches or less long, on short petioles parallel to stem or the upper ones sessile, the lobes usually again divided: flowers few terminating the forks so that the plant may be covered with bloom in its season, blue or blue-purple but varying to rose and white, 1¾ inches or less long, the slender acute somewhat bent spreading spur exceeding the oblong obtuse or short-acute sepals; petals blue or yellowish, united into a single body or bee which is lobed: follicle single, glabrous, about ½ inch long and thrice longer than broad, bearing an abrupt point on one margin; seeds angled, prominently squamate with concentric points and plates.—*D. Consolida*, Linnaeus 1753; *Consolida regalis*, S. F. Gray 1821.

Throughout Europe in fields, in Russia and Asia Minor; sometimes spontaneous in North America and elsewhere; seldom cultivated. This plant has a long history and is described by the herbalists; and it is to this day made the basis of a separate genus, Consolida, by certain botanists (see page 80).

crassifolium. Stem simple from a short thick root, pilose, to 1½ feet tall: leaves basal except perhaps one or two little ones on the stem, rounded in outline, to 4 inches across, blades cut half or more their depth into broad cuneate lobes that are bluntly toothed on the ends, sinuses very narrow, upper and under surfaces loosely hairy: flowers light blue, about 1 inch long, in open terminal raceme, on erect simple-bracted pedicels and standing crosswise with the sharp curved spur prominent; sepals short-acute, equalling spur or little shorter; bee prominently dark purple, the upper petals long-hairy and lower ones barbed: follicles 3, glabrous; seeds squamate.—*D. crassifolium*, Schrader 1818.

Turkestan, Siberia, China; at one time planted in the United States.

cucullatum. Tall and leafy to 8 feet, stems many from a woody root, glabrous below but pubescent in the inflorescence which is a closely flowered spiciform raceme with short ascending pedicels: leaves *elatum*-like, to 6 or 7 inches across, finely pubescent, in 3–7 divisions which are irregularly cut: flowers small, yellowish-white to bluish, pubescent, about ¾ inch long, standing crosswise or somewhat declined; the nearly or quite blunt sepals all cucullate or hooded (as if closed) and shorter than the stout thick spur; petals small and blue, the lower ones slenderly clawed: follicles 3, pubescent.—*D. cucullatum*, A. Nelson 1900.

Western Wyoming.

cultorum. Name proposed by A. Voss in 1896 (Vilmorin's Blumengaertneri, i, p. 36; ii, t. 4 fig. 15) for the assembly of delphiniums known to cultivators as *D. hybridum*, in view of the fact that the *hybridum* of Willdenow, a wild species, is much older. The forms included under *D. cultorum* are so diverse and may represent such inharmonious races that latterly I have not used the name. However, Voss undoubtedly had in mind the *elatum* set of hybrids or variants, as indicated by his remarks and picture, and if we wish to apply a Latin binomial to these forms we may employ his name, *cultorum:* see *D. hybridum*.

dasyanthum. Leafy larkspur, stem to 1½ feet tall, mostly simple, pubescent: leaves lightly pubescent, lower ones on very long petioles, blade about as broad as long, deeply divided, the parts broadly 3-lobed and sharply incised or cut, the upper ones on stem becoming nearly simple and broad-lanceolate: inflorescence a simple or nearly simple terminal raceme of few or not numerous flowers on slender prominently bracted pedicels; flowers pubescent, light blue with lighter splashes, the sepals to 2 inches long and acuminate; spur short, straight, not equalling the sepals; petals brownish, the lower ones bearded: follicles 3, hirsute; seeds lamellate or bearing plates crosswise.—*D. dasyanthum*, Karelin & Kirilow 1842.

Turkestan, western India; sometimes considered to be a variety of *D. caucasicum* which, in turn, is here treated as part of *D. speciosum*. The true plant is probably little known in cultivation.

decorum. Rather weak, 5–24 inches high, stem mostly glabrous, simple or moderately branched, rising from a tuberous root-cluster: leaves somewhat succulent and mostly radical or near the base, long-stalked, orbicular to reniform in outline, 1–2½ inches across, glabrous, divided to middle or beyond into 3–7 broad obtuse parts that are often again cleft or toothed: inflorescence of very open racemes 2–10 inches long, the slender upright-spreading pedicels 2 inches or less long, glabrous or pubescent, bearing very small bracts; flowers purplish-blue, nearly or quite glabrous, about ¾ inch long; spur horizontal or upturned, about equalling the oval sepals; petals brownish tinted blue, lower ones yellow-bearded: follicles 3, glabrous, about ½ inch long, veiny; seeds squamate.—*D. decorum*, Fischer & Meyer 1837.

Woodsy places and canyons, California. Attractive little plant, useful in wild-garden or rock-garden. I have seen one of the *elatum*-like larkspurs grown under the name *decorum*.

Delavayi. Tall, leafy, stem hairy and simple or branched: leaves long-stalked, pubescent, 5-parted to base, the divisions broadly rhomboid and variously cut-lobed: inflorescence of narrow many-flowered racemes, the erect pedicels pubescent; flowers blue, pubescent; spur about 1 inch long and much exceeding the broadly ovate sepals; upper petals glabrous and truncate, lower ones ciliate: follicles 3, erect, lightly setose.—*D. Delavayi*, Franchet 1886.

Yunnan, China, collected along small streams by J. M. Delavay. Little known in cultivation, the plant so called apparently an *elatum* derivative. Leaves of the true plant have short nearly or quite obtuse ultimate lobes.

delicatum: once grown in the United States; to be referred to *D. urceolatum*.

depauperatum. Nearly simple, to about 18 inches or more tall, from a tuberous cluster, more or less closely viscid-puberulent: leaves long-petioled, mostly radical or toward base of stem; blade orbicular to reniform in outline, 1–2 inches broad, cleft into 3 or 5 lobes which are again obtusely divided or notched; stem-leaves with very narrow final divisions: flowers dark rich blue to purple, few widely separated on slender pedicels in terminal racemes, ¾–1¼ inches long, slightly bent; spur standing nearly or quite horizontal and exceeding the broad blunt sepals; petals yellowish or two of them blue, not bearded: follicles 3, about ½ inch long, viscid-pubescent.—*D. depauperatum*, Nuttall 1838; *D. pauciflorum* var. *depauperatum*, Gray 1887.

Idaho, Oregon, California. Slender pretty plant, blooming early.

dictyocarpum. Plant to 2 feet, perhaps more, branched, leafy, nearly glabrous to hairy-pubescent: leaves 5–7-lobed, the parts oblong acutely cut, the upper ones about 3-parted and narrow parts nearly entire: inflorescence open and branched; flowers blue and glabrous (except in var. *pubiflorum*); spur straight; sepals twice longer than the blue petals: follicles 3, reticulate (whence the name *dictyocarpum:* netted fruit), and margins ciliate.—*D. dictyocarpum*, De Candolle 1818; *D. ciliatum* var. *dictyocarpum*, Huth 1895.

Siberia. Plants cultivated under this name may be wrongly determined.

discolor: an old horticultural name without definition and therefore untenable; applied to an *elatum* form.

divaricatum. Much-branched diffuse closely pubescent annual to 2 feet tall, the slender branches divaricate or widely spreading: leaves small, 1–2 inches across, divided into many short linear lobes after the manner of *D. Ajacis:* flowers violet, few together, scattered on the ends of branches, 1½ inches or less long, standing horizontally on their long pubescent small-bracted pedicels; spur slender and pointed, much exceeding the broad nearly obtuse sepals; petals yellowish, 3-lobed: follicle single, pubescent, rather slender; seeds shaggy with concentric plates.—*D. divaricatum*, Ledebour 1831; *D. Consolida* var. *divaricatum*, Huth 1895.

Russia, Armenia, Persia; little grown.

Duhmbergii. Leafy, to 2 feet, the stem hairy below and nearly glabrous at the top: leaves 5–7-parted, glabrous above and hairy on margins and on nerves underneath, the divisions cuneate and cut: inflorescence a many-flowered strict raceme; flowers blue or white, glabrous; spur about 1½ inches long, straight, about equalling the ovate or elliptic sepals; petals brownish, the upper ones slightly pilose at apex: follicles 3, about ⅓ inch long, glabrous; seeds narrowly winged, not squamate.—*D. Duhmbergii*, Huth 1893.

Russia and Siberia; collected in 1881 in the Altai Mountains by Duhmberg and others.

elatum. CANDLE LARKSPUR. Frontispiece. Plates 14, 15, 16, 17. Spicate strict-growing tall perennial, to 3 feet or more high, more or less pubescent to nearly glabrous: leaves large, palmately 5–7-parted nearly or quite to the base, or the upper ones 3-parted, the parts slashed into sharp lobes, petiole of lower leaves equalling or exceeding the blade: inflorescence primarily dense, erect and spiciform terminating the main axis, rising much above the foliage at maturity, and secondarily or subsequently lateral branches appearing below it; flowers blue, small in the wild plant (1–1¼ inches lengthwise), standing more or less crosswise; spur straight, about equalling the sepals which are glabrous, not widely spreading, blunt; petals (bee) dark or dull purple, the lower 2 notched and yellowish-barbed; pedicels 1 inch or less long, most of them bearing 2 small bracts near the middle and in the axil of an entire bract: follicles 3, glabrous, ½–¾ inch long at maturity; seeds 3-angled, broadly winged, not squamate but more or less rugose.—*D. elatum*, Linnæus 1753, habitat in Siberia.

var. **alpinum.** Plant leafy up to the inflorescence, tall: lower bracts (under pedicels) divided, often giving the spike a foliate look.—*D. alpinum*, Waldstein & Kitaibel 1812; *D. intermedium* var. *alpinum*, De Candolle 1824. *D. elatum* var. *alpinum*, Hegi.

Pyrenees across Europe to Turkestan, central Asia, Siberia, and Mongolia, in several forms or varieties.

This delphinium (*D. elatum*) has been an inhabitant of gardens for centuries and in the course of its cultivation has varied into many forms. It is a familiar inhabitant of premises and yards, usually in clear blues with prominent black eye. If this old garden plant has crossed with other species, the evidences are not clear. Perhaps *D. elatum*, as customarily defined by systematists, is a group rather than a definitive species. To this group belong the tall stately plants bearing terminal spikes with which delphinium experts are chiefly concerned. In some of the cultivated forms the bee has lost its dark color, but this departure may lie within the range of direct variation. Thus, one of the native varieties (var. *pyramidatum*) has a pyramidal-paniculate inflorescence, another (var. *pubiflorum*) has pubescent flowers, a third (var. *anomalum*) has modified color combinations in the bee. The plant needs study in the wild in respect to departures it might be expected to make under cultivation and selection.

The departures in cultivation are of course extensive and often significant, even aside from size and color of flowers. Thus, the spikes themselves vary so much in form that gardeners are able to classify them as columnar, spire-like, short-cylindrical, pyramidal. Comparative compactness or openness of the spike is an essential mark in Candle larkspurs, as well as cut and hang of foliage and natural vigor.

In recent time this delphinium has been the basis of great departures in garden varieties and strains, with hybridization entering into the progeny so miscellaneously that parentages may not be discernible. Some of the current varieties can hardly be referred to species. The cultivated sorts of the Elatum class are likely to be called *Delphinium hybridum* by breeders and growers, but that name is not available for such usage: see *D. hybridum*, page 98.

elongatum. Tall plant, somewhat hairy toward the top: divisions of leaf-blade about 7, under surface glabrous and glaucous, the final lobes lanceolate and acute: flowers dark blue, the sepals oval and about ½ inch long; petals color of sepals: follicles 3, about ¾ inch long, hairy-pubescent.—*D. elongatum*, Rydberg 1902.

Hills and mountains, Alberta to Colorado.

exaltatum. Plate 20. Strong but slender, to 5 feet and more, with short thick root-crown and fibrous roots, stem glabrous (unless at top) and well foliaged: leaves as broad as long in outline or sometimes broader, reniform to open-cordate at base, thinly pubescent on both surfaces, parted almost to the petiole into 3 main narrow divisions (1 inch or less broad at widest part) and the lateral divisions again deeply parted, the divisions 3–5-lobed into prominent and often sharp points: flowers hairy-pubescent, small, total length about ¾ inch, standing crosswise or declined in long open racemes terminating the main and lateral axes, dull blue-purple and not showy, the ascending pubescent pedicels becoming an inch or so long and bracted near the the top; spur essentially straight and equalling or somewhat exceeding the sepals which are broad and obtuse; bee shorter than sepals, colored like them except for the prominent white beard, anthers many: follicles 3, about ½ inch long, beaked, pubescent; seeds 3-angled and white-winged, not puckered or squamate.—*D. exaltatum*, Aiton 1789.

Widespread but not ubiquitous from Pennsylvania to Alabama, Minnesota and Nebraska. It is asserted that this North American larkspur has entered into the horticultural races by hybridization, but I have found no evidence of it. Philip Miller grew it direct from seeds

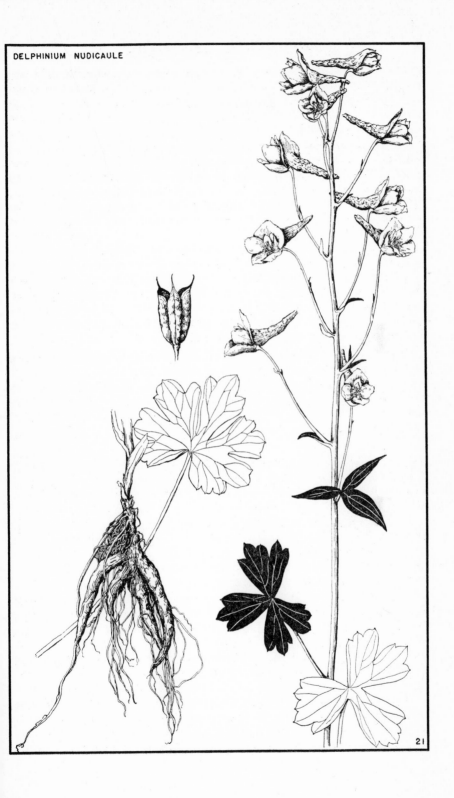

21

sent him by John Bartram of Philadelphia, and Aiton makes no statement of its being otherwise in cultivation. The flowers are too small and too indifferent in color to suggest a showy garden plant. From a European botanic garden I have a plant, collected in 1925, under the name *hybridum* that is indistinguishable from *D. exaltatum* except that it is glabrous, flowers a little larger and lighter blue.

fissum. Slender, pubescent, 2–3 feet tall from a thick clustered root, stem more or less leafy: leaves rounded in outline but cut to base into many very narrow segments that are nearly linear, petioles all long: inflorescence a rather close terminal spike above the foliage; flowers azure-blue, standing crosswise; spur straight, somewhat longer than the sepals; upper petals blue at the tips, the lower ones bearded: follicles 3, either glabrous or hairy; seeds 3-angled, scaly in rings.— *D. fissum*, Waldstein & Kitaibel 1802.

Southeastern Europe. Considered by Huth to be a synonym of *D. hybridum*, Stephan, but that binomial cannot hold as we learn in the discussion of *hybridum* page 98, and other old binomials applied to the plant may be in doubt; therefore for this occasion I use *fissum*. The species is infrequent in cultivation.

formosum of cultivators is not one thing. Most of it is *D. cheilanthum* var. *formosum*, which see on page 88.

The *formosum* of botanical literature is a species of the *elatum* set. It is a tall perennial with thick stem hairy toward base and strong purple-blue flowers, spur scarcely exceeding the sepals, prominent dark purple petals (or bee) of which the upper 2 are yellow at tip and the lower ones orange-barbed: follicles pubescent; seeds squamate in ridges: leaves 5–7-palmately parted or the cauline ones 3–5-parted, the segments cut.—*D. formosum*, Boissier & Huet 1856.

Caucasus region, where it is showy late in summer in the high valleys, said to prefer non-lime formations. I have not seen this species in cultivation unless in botanic gardens. The horticultural *D. formosum* pictured by Regel in Gartenflora in 1859 and the one in Flore des Serres, 1857, are of later date than the botanically established and different *formosum* of Boissier & Huet.

Gayanum: see discussion under *D. Ajacis.*

Geyeri. Closely pubescent or tomentose, herbage with a whitish look or sometimes violet-tinged, 12–18 inches high less or more, with a cluster of deep woody roots: leaves somewhat fleshy, mostly at or near the base and then very long-petioled, the blade parted into many obtusish segments ¼ inch and less broad, each tipped with a callus: inflorescence open or dense terminal spiciform racemes, the stout pedicels bearing 1 or 2 bracts near the top; flowers azure-blue, 1 inch and more long, standing crosswise or somewhat inclined, showy; spur straight or frequently bent toward the end, exceeding or equalling the broad obtuse sepals; petals blue, whitish-bearded.—*D. Geyeri*, Greene 1894; bears the name of Karl A. Geyer, German botanist who travelled in North America a century ago and who collected this species.

High plains in Wyoming, Colorado and Utah; one of the cattle poisons; abundant.

glareosum: *D. bicolor.*

glaucum: *D. scopulorum* var.

grandiflorum. BOUQUET LARKSPUR. Plate 10. Forking or branching perennial, usually short-lived, 1½–3 feet tall, from a tap or forked root, the slightly angled slender stems lightly pubescent: leaves relatively small, dull green, the lower ones 3–4 inches across, glabrous or essentially so, orbicular to reniform in outline, multipartite, the 5 or more main divisions ½ inch or less broad at widest part and commonly less than ¼ inch, the divisions again narrowly lobed, upper ones reduced to a few linear parts: inflorescence branched and very open, composed of many short few-flowered racemes in a paniculate system but typically with a long central axis, pedicels 2-bracted toward the top and axillary to a simple or forked bract; flowers blue, purplish-blue, 1–2 inches long over all and variable in size, standing crosswise or declined, spur very prominent and straight or very nearly so and equalling or exceeding the length of the sepals (remainder of the flower); sepals ovate, acute to obtuse, each bearing a gland near the tip; bee large, color of the sepals, upper pair of petals small, lower pair bulging and bearing light yellow tufts on sides at base: follicles 3, pubescent, less than 1 inch long, with wide-spreading points; seeds 3-angled and thin-edged, not squamate.—*D. grandiflorum*, Linnæus 1753; *D. chinense*, Fischer 1808; *D. grandiflorum* var. *chinense*, Fischer & DeCandolle 1824; *D. sinense*, Hort.

Siberia, Mongolia, China, in several forms.

Showy species, with large brilliant well separated flowers; airy and decorative; variations occur in color, in size of flower, and in width of leaf divisions. Now and then two colors appear on one plant. Plants sometimes grown as *D. grandiflorum* may be large-flowered forms of the *D. cheilanthum* group. Type specimen of *D. grandiflorum* in the Linnean herbarium shows a plant with strong middle stem overtopping the slender side shoots and bearing 10 or a dozen flowers closer together than in Plate 11.

Several horticultural variants are listed. Var. **azureum** is light blue; var. **album** is white; var. **pumilum** is dwarf, only 6 inches or less high.

halteratum. Annual, much like *D. cardiopetalum* but lower petals truncate; plant likely to be less paniculately forked and not so leafy.— *D. halteratum*, Sibthorp & Smith 1806–9.

Widespread in the Mediterranean region; probably not in cultivation, its place being taken by the more floriferous *D. cardiopetalum.*

Hansenii. Mostly simple, from a cluster of tubers, slender when only a foot or 2 tall but sometimes to 4 feet, thinly hairy-pubescent, the long petioles long-hairy: leaves largely basal, divided into many linear or narrow-oblong lobes, 2 inches across more or less; stem-leaves smaller and divisions fewer: inflorescence very long, either open-flowered or moderately dense terminal mostly slender racemes, the rather short pubescent pedicels narrowly 2-bracted near apex; flowers variable in color, from pale blue to pink and lavender, sometimes white, about 1 inch long, usually somewhat declined; spur mostly a little curved toward tip, longer than the broad obtuse sepals; petals colored like the sepals, the bee bearded: follicles 3, pubescent, beaked, about ¾ inch long at maturity; seeds squamate.— *D. Hansenii*, Greene 1896; *D. hesperium* var. *Hansenii*, Greene 1892, having been collected by George Hansen.

Foothills of the Sierras, central California, and a variety in more elevated areas.

hesperium. Variable species with a woody clustered root or sometimes a tap-root, finely pubescent, to 3 feet tall, stem usually simple: leaves all along the stem but the upper ones much smaller, all divided into either broad (½ inch) or narrow parts that are again obtusely lobed or notched: inflorescence a moderately dense raceme, the pedicels short, about ½ inch except the lower ones and strongly ascending with narrow bracts about midway; flowers mostly blue but in other shades to white, more or less pubescent, about ¾–1 inch long, standing nearly crosswise; sepals broad, obtuse or short-acute, somewhat shorter than the straight or only slightly curved spur; petals same color as sepals and nearly equalling them, bearded: follicles 3, pubescent, ½ inch or less long; seeds whitish, angled and winged.— *D. hesperium*, Asa Gray 1887.

California; coast ranges from central part northward; attractive slender species.

hybridum. We invite confusion when we speak of *Delphinium hybridum*. At least three things are involved.

To the horticulturist *hybridum* means the general class of admixtures and nondescripts in the Candle larkspur group, associated with the binomial *D. elatum*. It is used as a general term, no particular variant being meant. The name therefore lacks precision and cannot be defined; under Rules of nomenclature it falls. A more definite obstacle is the fact that a technically defined *D. hybridum*, a very different plant, dates from 1799. If the horticulturist desires a substitute for his *hybridum*, he may use *D. cultorum*.

This earlier *hybridum* was described by Willdenow, a plant known to him from Siberia. The name was proposed to him by Stephan in a letter. The epithet *hybridum* does not necessarily imply that the plant was a hybrid. Willdenow merely questions whether it may have been a variety, but of what relationship he does not imply; he gives it the vernacular (German) name Bastard rittersporn, intended probably only as a translation of the Latin word. This plant of Stephan and Willdenow is native in southeastern Europe east of the Adriatic, to

Turkestan, Russia and Siberia. We are about to learn there is a still earlier *D. hybridum*, so the Willdenow plant must bear the next oldest tenable name; what this name shall be is perhaps not established under current Rules, but in this Enumeration it is entered as *Delphinium fissum*.

This still earlier *D. hybridum* dates from Antoine Goüan in his Illustrationes et Observationes Botanicæ published in 1773 at Tiguri (Zurich). He gives a full description. He grew the plant from seeds sent to him by Linnæus and quotes what the donor said in the letter of October 1762. The seeds from Linnæus probably bore the name *D. hybridum;* Linnæus had used the epithet in print and had supposed his plant to be a hybrid between *Delphinium elatum* and *Aconitum Napellus*, but this was prior to 1753 the year from which binomial nomenclature is dated. His subsequent use of the epithet is without description; he did not take it up in Species Plantarum, but he left a good specimen marked in his own hand (a photograph of it is before me), which DeCandolle long ago affirmed is *D. villosum* (described as late as 1818). What the final adjustment of names shall be awaits the monographer who has both records and specimens before him; for our purpose it is enough to explain why the horticulturist may not use the epithet *hybridum* for the plants to which he customarily applies it.

inimitabile: large-flowered dark purple form, in cultivation, of the *elatum* or Candle larkspur kind.

intermedium: one of the native forms of *D. elatum*.

Lamartinii: a garden blue-flowered variety of the *D. cheilanthum* var. *formosum* type that originated with Lemoine in Nancy, France, previous to 1905; name is still current. A living plant before me as I write has foliage and racemes of the *D. cheilanthum* kind; flowers nearly violet ultramarine and 1¾ inches long; upper petals nearly white and narrow; lower petals ultramarine but bearing heavy yellow beard; a handsome larkspur.

laxiflorum: *D. villosum* var.; but the plant I have seen cultivated under the name *laxiflorum* is wholly incorrect, being apparently one of the Garland or Candle set.

Leonardii: *D. Andersonii*.

leucophæum: *D. Menziesii* var. *ochroleucum*.

likiangense. Stem somewhat scape-like, 4–8 inches high, sometimes to 15 inches, the plant nearly glabrous, roots long and running deep: leaves nearly all radical and long-petioled, blade many-parted, lobes oblong and pointed, passing into 3-parted and lanceolate bracts: flowers rich blue to lilac, somewhat pubescent, nearly bell-shaped, 2–5 on a stem or scape, standing above the foliage; spur straight, thick, about 1 inch long, not equalling or at least not surpassing the ovate sepals; petals lilac, the lower ones bearded and ciliate: follicles 3, hirsute.—*D. likiangense*, Franchet 1893.

High mountains in Likiang range, Yunnan, China; a rock-garden or alpine-garden plant of great beauty.

luteum: *D. nudicaule* var.

Maackianum. One of the Elatum group, from which is it particularly distinguished by the ultimate lobes of the leaf being blunt rather than sharp and laciniate, blade often reniform at base and lightly pubescent on both surfaces, racemes less densely flowered so that they are hardly spiciform and arranged on several long branches in addition to the central or axial one, making a paniculate arrangement in mature plants, the branches densely yellow-hairy, upper petals very small and the lower ones densely hairy, follicles mostly larger at maturity, seeds small, squamate. The plant in nature reaches about 3 feet high, branched above, glabrous below but hirsute on the branches: leaves reniform at base or sometimes truncate, pubescent above and underneath, 3–5-parted: inflorescence loosely paniculate, with ovate-lanceolate and often blue-colored bracts; flowers blue, the spur straight or curved and exceeding the sepals (to ¾ inch long), bee conspicuous and dull purple but the 2 upper petals very small: follicles 3, erect, glabrous, the points spreading; seeds small, squamose or scaly.—*D. Maackinaum*, Regel 1861; dedicated to Richard Maack, Russian botanist.

Eastern Siberia, in two or three forms.

The binomial *Delphinium Maackianum* has long been in the trade. I grew plants so named many years ago. Yet I have rarely seen a cultivated plant true to the name; the stock belongs to other forms of the Elatum-Cheilanthum groups.

macrocentron. Hairy perennial to 5 feet, somewhat branched, leafy in lower part: leaves 5–7-parted and the narrow divisions notched or cut into acute and acuminate lobes, the primary segments 1 inch or less broad, the upper stem-leaves with long narrow entire divisions: inflorescence of loose few-flowered racemes high above the foliage, pedicels recurved at the top so that the long flower is pendent; flowers hairy, blue and green or yellow and green, whitish at tips, about 2 inches long, the yellow stamens nearly as long as the broad obtuse sepals; spur big and stout, standing straight up, equalling or exceeding the sepals, broad, obtuse at tip where it is briefly curved; petals narrower than sepals: follicles 3, hairy.—*D. macrocentron*, Oliver 1885.

Mountains in eastern tropical Africa, to 8,000 feet, chiefly in Uganda. Plant with singular flowers.

Menziesii. Low, from a cluster of short tubers, 15 inches or less tall, stem finely pubescent, leafy, simple or frequently branched at the base or middle: leaves glabrous or pubescent, divided and cleft into oblong or linear more or less obtuse lobes: inflorescence a terminal mostly open raceme, bearing few or many flowers, pedicels to 1 or 2 inches long and spreading or upwardly arching; flowers blue, sparsely

pubescent, 1½ inches or less long and nearly or quite as broad; spur straight or slightly bent, equalling or exceeding the sepals which are narrow-ovate to oblong and blunt or only indifferently acute; petals blue, nearly as long as sepals, lower ones bearded: follicles 3, lightly hairy to practically glabrous, about ¾ inch long, divergent from base; seeds margined at the ends.—*D. Menziesii*, DeCandolle 1818; dedicated to Archibald Menzies, physician and early collector in North America; *D. Nelsonii*, Greene 1896.

Northern California to Utah and Montana and British Columbia.

var. **ochroleucum,** from the Willamette Valley, Oregon, has cream-colored sepals, and blue petals bordered white.—*D. Menziesii* var. *ochroleucum*, Nuttall ex Torrey & Gray 1838; *D. ochroleucum*, Hort.; *D. leucophæum*, Greene 1895.

Moerheimii. Variety originated at the Moerheim Nurseries in Holland; it is a pure white Belladonna type. See page 72.

montanum. Low and mostly simple-stemmed, 20 inches or less high: leaves pubescent on both surfaces, parted nearly to base and the parts cut into oblong lobes; lower bracts many-parted, upper ones linear, pedicels hirsute, the inflorescence many-flowered on ends of branches: flowers pale blue; sepals narrow, pubescent outside, soon falling; petals dark purple, the lower ones barbate; spur straight or the apex incurved and equalling the sepals: follicles yellow-pilose when young; seeds somewhat winged on margins, not squamate.—*D. montanum*, De Candolle 1815.

Mountains, Spain, France, Italy, Switzerland, Tyrol. The plant sometimes cultivated as *D. montanum* may not be true to name.

Nelsonii: *D. Menziesii.*

Nortonianum: *D. carolinianum* var.

nudicaule. RED LARKSPUR. Plate 21. Stem glabrous, more or less glaucous, 1–2½ feet tall from a cluster of thick long roots, leaves mostly radical: leaves somewhat fleshy, either glabrous or with few short hairs, 3-parted into broad obtuse divisions that are variously toothed or notched and the lateral ones perhaps deeply parted: inflorescence a long very open raceme, pedicels slender and widely diverging; flowers brick-red, glabrous to sparsely short-hairy, 1¼–1½ inches long, standing oblique or up-and-down, showy; spur straight or upcurved, longer than the broad obtuse or very short-acute sepals; petals much shorter than sepals, yellowish except perhaps at tip, not bearded: follicles 3, curving after maturity, glabrous to pubescent.—*D. nudicaule*, Torrey & Gray 1838.

California, from central part north in coast ranges and Sierra Nevadas; a handsome plant with its pendent flowers, hardy in the Northeast but not likely to attain its best stature; supposed to be a parent in the newer red horticultural varieties, p. 70.

var. **luteum.** Flowers pale yellow, mostly larger and pubescent, with broader spur.—*D. nudicaule* var. *luteum*, Jepson 1923; *D. luteum*, Heller, 1903.

Coastal country, central California. Variations to yellow in the garden are not necessarily to be taken as representing the native var. *luteum*.

Nuttallii. To 20 inches or more tall, root tuberous and fascicled, herbage more or less glaucous, stem nearly or quite glabrous below but pubescent and perhaps viscid above: leaves 3–5-parted and the parts again divided into many oblong or linear segments: flowers indigo-blue, in a spiciform raceme, lightly puberulent; spur straight, about ¾ inch long and exceeding the broad sepals; petals blue but upper ones yellowish below tip, bearded: follicles 3, pubescent, about ½ inch long, erect; seeds winged, not squamate.—*D. Nuttallii*, Asa Gray 1887; *D. columbianum*, Greene 1894; dedicated to Thomas Nuttall, 1786-1859, who wrote on North American plants.

Open places and meadows, Oregon, Washington. E. L. Greene proposed the name *columbianum* for this species inasmuch as there is an earlier *Nuttallianum* (Pritzel 1843) in the genus although apparently not regularly published, but under current Rules the names *Nuttallii* and *Nuttallianum* do not conflict. *D. Nuttalianum* appears not to be in cultivation; considered by Gray to be *D. pauciflorum*, Nutt.

occidentale. Glabrous below but pubescent in inflorescence, leafy, 3 feet or more tall: leaves large, to 6 inches across, pubescent on both surfaces, parted into 3–7 much-cleft main divisions that are mostly broad: inflorescence a many-flowered mostly long raceme that is often branched; flowers dark blue, viscid-pubescent outside, about ¾ inch long, standing crosswise on short pedicels; spur straight or perhaps curved at tip, longer than the obtuse or acute sepals; upper petals yellowish tipped blue entire, lower ones acutely lobed: follicles 3, about ¾ inch long.—*D. occidentale*, Watson 1880.

Mountains, Colorado, Utah, Wyoming, Idaho.

ochroleucum: *D. Menziesii* var. *ochroleucum*, once advertized in Oregon. The *ochroleucum* of botanists (Steven 1818) of Asia, is apparently not in cultivation; it grows to about 3 feet tall, leafy, flowers milk-white to yellowish, spur straight and exceeding the ovate sepals which are less than ½ inch long, petals yellowish, the lower ones bearded.

orientale. Plate 7. Annual, like *D. Ajacis* but the flowers violet-purple and smaller; bractlet on the pedicel usually longer than in that species and nearer the flower although this character is not uniform: spur short, declined, shorter than sepals or not exceeding them: color of the flower is a dependable mark of *D. orientale*, and it appears not to vary greatly. Plant to 30 inches tall, from a slender tap-root but which sometimes branches, stem closely hairy-pubescent, branching but maintaining a main central straight axis, racemes slender and open: flowers nearly or quite 1 inch long and of similar size in expansion, the straight or slightly curved spur shorter than the broad obtuse sepals: follicle single, pubescent, about ¾ inch long at maturity; seeds triangular, squamate.—*D. orientale*, Gay 1839.

Fields in southern and central Europe, north Africa, Asia. Distinctions between *D. orientale* and *D. Ajacis* are yet to be cleared, in the cultivated stocks.

oxysepalum. Very leafy, nearly or quite simple, 5–20 inches tall, lightly pubescent to nearly glabrous: leaves long-stalked, the blade cordate-orbicular in outline, 2–4 inches across, 3-parted and the lateral divisions usually again parted, sinuses very narrow so that the divisions are close together, margins lobed ½ inch deep more or less, the lobes nearly obtuse: inflorescence a short rather close raceme of a dozen or fewer flowers that stand close to the upper leaves, pedicels pubescent and provided with long linear bracts; flowers blue, large, about 1½ inches long, the curved or even hooked acute spur shorter than the large broad acute or short-acuminate sepals; petals dark colored, much shorter than the prominent sepals, lower ones bearded: follicles 3, short, glabrous or nearly so.—*D. oxysepalum*, Pax & Borbas 1890.

Central and eastern Europe in mountains. Abundantly foliaged plant with declined or drooping large flowers.

palmatum: *D. elatum.*

paniculatum. Diffusely branching finely pubescent annual, root small and fibrous, 1–3 feet and more tall: leaves along the stem after the radical ones perish but small, mostly not exceeding 2 inches across, parted to the base into linear acute divisions: flowers deep blue or blue-violet, about 1 inch long and standing crosswise at ends of the slender branches; spur straight or upcurved, very sharp, exceeding the broad short-acute sepals; petals 3-lobed, much shorter than sepals: follicle 1, glabrous, about ⅓ inch long, twice longer than broad and thus differing from *D. Consolida* as well as in the much smaller flowers.—*D. paniculatum*, Host 1831.

Southeastern Europe, Asia Minor.

Parishii. Stem to 30 inches tall, glabrous, mostly simple or only sparingly branched and not leafy, from a forked thick somewhat fleshy root: leaves thickish, mostly basal, 2 inches or less across, twice cleft into narrow parts that may be either obtuse or acute and that are sometimes only linear: inflorescence a long and sparsely flowered raceme to 10 or 12 inches, the glabrous stout pedicels bracted at or near the top; flowers light azure-blue to whitish, standing crosswise or ascending, about ¾ inch long, the lightly curved stout spur about equalling the broad obtuse sepals; petals somewhat shorter than the sepals: follicles 3, somewhat pubescent, about ½ inch long; seeds whitish, with narrow wings.—*D. Parishii*, Asa Gray 1887; dedicated to S. B. Parish, California botanist.

Washes and hills, southern California; in desert regions lower areas, and up to 7,500 feet; early.

Parryi. Stems to 3 feet, minutely pubescent, mostly simple, not very leafy, from a hard straight or forked not fleshy root: leaves both basal and cauline, to 3 inches across, cleft into several or many narrow or even linear or filiform lobes and sometimes pedate: inflorescence a raceme usually rather closely flowered but sometimes open, the pubescent pedicles bracted at top; flowers purplish or deep blue, pubescent, standing practically crosswise, about 1 inch long; spur straight or lightly curved, about equalling the broad obtuse sepals; petals lighter colored than sepals and shorter: follicles 3, about ½ inch long, lightly pubescent; seeds whitish only on angles.—*D. Parryi*, Gray 1887; collected by C. C. Parry (1823–1890) as early as 1850.

Southern California, dry areas in coastal regions; early.

Penardii: *D. virescens* var.

Przewalskii. Small plant, glabrous and erect, 6–10 inches tall, branched at base: leaves glabrous, strongly 3–5-parted, the divisions deeply cut, ultimate parts obtuse: flowers blue, mostly terminal; spur straightish or arched, about ¾ inch long, equalling the sepals; upper petals dark brownish and glabrous, lower petals white-ciliate and yellow bearded: follicles 3, densely hairy.—*D. Przewalskii*, Huth 1895.

Western Mongolia, where it was collected by Przewalski in 1871 and 1873. Plants I have seen in cultivation as *Przewalskii* are misnamed. The true plant is a small rock-garden subject.

pumilum: the trade name apparently refers to dwarf forms, white-flowered and blue-flowered, of *D. grandiflorum*.

Pylzowii. Dwarf from a long horizontal or oblique woody root, silky-pubescent, leafy, 6–10 inches tall: leaves long-stalked, orbicular to reniform in outline, 1–2 inches across, divided one-half or depth of the blade into lobes obtuse or only short-acute, or the stem-leaves into linear more acute parts: flowers very large, 1 or 2 or 3 on a stem, deep purple, to 2½ inches long; spur straight or curved toward end, equalling or exceeding the pilose broadly-ovate short-acute or blunted sepals; petals dark violet, upper ones glabrous and lower ones hairy: follicles 5, densely hairy.—*D. Pylzowii*, Maximowicz 1876.

Western China at high altitudes, on limestone. A handsome rock-garden or alpine-garden subject; plants I have seen cultivated as *Pylzowii* are tall and of the Garland group. Writing in England, 1937, Sampson Clay says: "every catalogue and every Botanic Garden list includes *D. Pylzowii*, but I greatly doubt if there is a living plant of it in Europe at the time of writing.'"

Requienii. Biennial of the Staphisagria group, 2 feet or less tall, hirsute, the stem leafy and not much branched: leaves large, to 10 inches across, deeply divided into usually 3 main parts and the lateral parts again divided, each segment strongly irregularly lobed from the end and the apices acute; uppermost leaves 3-parted: inflorescence open and branched, hairy; flowers blue, about 1 inch across, the lower ones on long hairy-pubescent pedicels; spur curved, about equalling the broad mostly obtuse sepals; petals large and prominent, the upper ones pale yellow suffused blue, lower ones obtuse and mostly exceeding the sepals: follicles 3, broad, ½ inch or more long. —*D. Requienii*, DeCandolle 1815; bears the name of Requien.

Southern France, Corsica, Sardinia, Balearic Islands; other plants are likely to be grown under this name.

reticulatum. Tall, to 3 or 4 feet, leafy-stemmed, glaucous and glabrous on lower part: leaves to 4 inches across, pubescent, 3–5-divided, the divisions broadly cuneate and again acutely cleft: inflorescence a raceme, practically simple; flowers small, dark blue sometimes streaked yellow, viscid-hairy outside; upper petals blue and perhaps streaked yellow, lower ones lobed: follicles 3, about ½ inch long.—*D. reticulatum*, Rydberg 1906.

Open woods, Wyoming, Idaho.

Ruysii. A recent series of hybrids between *Delphinium nudicaule* and a horticultural form of the Candle or Elatum class. The early experiments in the production of this series are recounted in the section on Red Larkspurs on page 70. We may now trace the origin of the binomial *Delphinium Ruysii*, which bears the name of B. Ruys, Director of the Royal Moerheim Nurseries at Dedemsvaart, Holland. Only one variety of this series, Pink Sensation, has yet been introduced.

In the Journal of the Royal Horticultural Society, London, for November, 1935, "a pink Delphinium of the Belladonna type," "result of a cross between *D. nudicaule* and *D. elatior*" (*elatum*) was figured under the name *Delphinium × Ruysii*.

That year, also, a communication was presented to the International Horticultural Congress at Rome, September 16–21, 1935, by the son, Dr. J. D. Ruys in collaboration with W. J. C. Lawrence of England, under the title "The Red Flowered Delphinium Ruysii; a New Species Cross." Cytological evidence was presented in confirmation of the hybrid origin. The variety Pink Sensation was not mentioned in the paper.

In 1936 Mr. Lawrence published his valuable article on The Origin of New Forms of Delphinium in Genetica. In it he mentions *Delphinium Ruysii* "a 'border' type *Delphinium* which segregates the new red-flowered forms." Lawrence's cytological studies indicate that *D. Ruysii* is result of hybridization between *D. nudicaule* and *D. elatum*.

In that year, also (1936), the Royal Moerheim Nurseries made a colored portrait of the variety and the plate was distributed in the autumn of 1937 in their jubilee catalogue; it was called "Delphinium Ruysii Pink Sensation (Ruys)." The binomial *Delphinium Ruysii* appeared again in Gardeners' Chronicle for April 2, 1938, with a horticultural account of Pink Sensation and a picture.

It is the intention of the originators to apply the name *D. Ruysii* to

23

the whole series of offspring from their *nudicaule* × *elatum* cross. The progeny will undoubtedly include many kinds worthy of asexual propagation. I have seen great numbers of them, yet unnamed, ranging through all the delphinium colors and in many statures and kinds of foliage.

scaposum. Stem scape-like, to 30 inches, leafy toward base, from clustered thick but not tuberous roots, glabrous: leaves small, 2 inches or less across, clustered at base, fleshy, glabrous, reniform in outline, 3-cleft and again divided into narrow blunt lobes: inflorescence a very open terminal raceme the lower pedicels of which are like long branches; flowers dark blue, about 1 inch long and standing crosswise on their stalks; spur about ½ inch long, straight or somewhat curved, about equalling or perhaps exceeding the obtuse or barely acute sepals; upper petals yellowish tinged blue, lower ones dark blue and lobed: follicles 3, about ½ inch long, glabrous or perhaps viscid and veiny.—*D. scaposum*, Greene 1881.

In dry land, Colorado to Arizona and New Mexico.

scopulorum. Tall very leafy-stemmed *elatum*-like nearly or quite glabrous plant, to 3 and 4 feet and more: leaves to 6 inches across, parted two-thirds or more to base of blade into 3 main sections and the lateral sections again cut so that the leaf is apparently primarily 5-parted, lobes again slashed into sharp points: inflorescence a rather dense simple spike-like raceme, the pedicels rather short; flowers blue to purplish, about ¾ inch long, standing crosswise in the cluster; spur straight or only slightly curved, equalling or a little exceeding the blunt sepals; upper petals yellowish but blue at tip, lower ones blue and white-barbed: follicles 3, to ¾ inch long, glabrous or lightly pubescent.—*D. scopulorum*, Asa Gray 1853.

Arizona and New Mexico; of wide western range in its varieties.

var. **glaucum.** Plant more or less glaucous.—*D. scopulorum* var. *glaucum*, Gray 1887; *D. glaucum*, Watson 1880.

Mountains, southern California to Alaska, above 6,000 feet in its southern ranges.

sibiricum: *D. grandiflorum.*

simplex. Stem variously pubescent to nearly glabrous below, viscid in the raceme, rising 6 inches to 2 feet from a close cluster of short tubers, little if at all branched, foliage mostly near the base: leaves thickish, lower ones 2 inches or less across, divided into several or many various obtuse lobes, those up the stem smaller and more narrowly cut: inflorescence a simple short or elongated narrow open raceme with short erect pedicels; flowers blue, about 1 inch long, standing crosswise, pubescent; sepals oblong, obtuse or nearly so, equalled or exceeded by the straight or curved acute spur; upper petals whitish at apex but bluish at base, prominent: follicles 3, pubescent, erect, about ½ inch long.—*D. simplex*, Douglas 1829.

Meadows in Wyoming, Oregon, Washington.

sinense: *D. grandiflorum.*

speciosum. Like *D. elatum* in size and appearance but differs decidedly in the seeds. In *D. elatum* the mature seeds may be indistinctly wrinkled or puckered but in *D. speciosum* they bear unmistakable imbricated scales; see *l* in Plate 2. *D. speciosum* is in cultivation in botanical collections and probably elsewhere. It is little branched, leafy, to 30 inches and more, stem distinctly striate and variously hirsute-pubescent: leaves hairy-pubescent, mainly 3-divided and again cut and notched into rather broad lobes with many sharp points: inflorescence a long rather dense spiciform raceme with often 2 and more pubescent erect pedicels at a node; flowers blue, 1¼ inches or more long, standing crosswise, the broad obtuse or nearly blunt veiny sepals equalled or perhaps exceeded by the bent or hooked spur; petals dark purple, the lower ones yellow-barbed: follicles 3, villous or becoming nearly glabrous, ½ inch or more long; seeds prominently squamate.—*D. speciosum,* Bieberstein 1808; *D. caucasicum,* Authors, but the *caucasicum* in cultivation is more likely to be *D. elatum.*

Southwestern Asia, in several forms and named botanical varieties.

Var. **glabratum,** presumably glabrous, is listed.

splendens: garden form of the *elatum* set.

Staphisagria. Stout soft-hairy leafy biennial to 3 feet or more, the stem thick and nearly fleshy: leaves 3–5 inches across, rather uniformly divided into 5 or more flat parts 1 inch or less broad that are only moderately lobed by big obtusish teeth: inflorescence a very open or straggling terminal raceme often branched at base, peduncles and pedicels soft-hairy; flowers blue often greenish-striped, and varying to pale tints, an inch or so across, pubescent; sepals obtuse and much exceeding the very short obtuse spur; petals large and flaring, conspicuous, whitish: follicles 3, very thick, taper-pointed, pubescent, about ¾ inch long and half as thick; seeds few, 3-angled, reticulate but not squamate.—*D. Staphisagria,* Linnæus 1753, being the Staphisagria of the herbalists and carrying an interesting history. It is the Stavesacre of English-speaking people, the seeds yielding the poisonous delphinine and have been employed against vermin and once in human uses; the Latin name is *Staphis agria,* wild Stavesacre.

Through southern Europe to Asia Minor; little planted but a curiosity (along with *D. Requienii*) among delphiniums because of the soft growth, open flower, scarcely distinguishable spur, and puffy few-seeded pods, as well as biennial duration.

subalpinum: *D. Barbeyi.*

sulphureum of botanists (Boissier & Haussknecht 1867) is an annual of Asia Minor apparently not in cultivation; *sulphureum* as cultivated is likely to be *D. Zalil.*

tatsienense. Much like *D. grandiflorum* but the flower arrangement all diffuse or of the corymbose type rather than centrally in a long raceme as is usual in well developed plants of the other species; spur also longer in proportion to the sepals and more definitely hooked at the end. *D. grandiflorum* in cultivation produces lateral floral branches as well as the axial raceme, and one of these branches may look like the usual cluster of *tatsienense*. In *D. tatsienense* the stem is openly forked and without a strong axial raceme, 2 feet and more tall: flowers violet-blue, about 1¼ inches long, standing crosswise in the pedicel; spur ¾–1 inch long, rather slender, downward curved or hooked at the end, exceeding the broad obtuse sepals that bear a spot near the end; upper petals dull yellowish, lower ones blue and yellow-bearded: follicles 3, pubescent, ½ inch or more long; seeds 3-angled and narrowly thin-winged.—*D. tatsienense*, Franchet 1893; name spelled *tatsiense* by the first monographer and this practice more or less continued, but the original author spelled it the longer way, from the region Ta-tsien-lou in Szechuan, western China where it was first found. It is a useful garden plant, readily raised from seeds.

tenuisectum. Stem 2–3 feet tall, angled and striate, leafy, obscurely puberulent, the root thick and somewhat woody: leaves many, very finely divided, short-stalked, with linear segments: flowers intensely blue, rather large, in a raceme about 1 foot long, the pedicels short and ascending; spur short and stout, nearly horizontal or ascending; petals hairy: follicles 3, puberulent, acute.—*D. tenuisectum*, Greene 1894.
Northern Mexico, New Mexico.

tiroliense is accredited a form of *D. villosum* from mountains of the Tyrol.—*D. villosum* var. *tiroliense*, Huth 1895; *D. tiroliense*, Dalla Torre 1873.

tricorne. Plate 23. Semi-succulent low leafy plant variable in color, mostly 6–18 inches tall but reported to 3 feet, usually glabrous but sometimes lightly pubescent, the usually simple stem rising from a cluster of tuberous roots: leaves long-stalked (except perhaps the uppermost), 2–4 inches broad and commonly not as long or at least length not exceeding breadth, glabrous, blade cut to base into 3 main parts and these again lobed and cut into short-acute segments that vary from linear to ½ inch broad: inflorescence a terminal raceme 1 foot or less long, the lower flowers often remote on long pedicels, apical part frequently dense, axis and pedicels likely to be pubescent; flowers ¾–1½ inches long, standing crosswise or declined, commonly blue but sometimes bluish and whitish, the straightish or curved spur about equalling the broad blunt generally glabrous sepals; petals much shorter than sepals and similarly colored, the lower ones bearded: follicles 3, glabrous or nearly so, about ½ inch long, widely diverged from the base at maturity and presenting a tricorne effect, with sharp points; seeds long, dark colored, not squamate.—*D. tricorne*, Michaux 1803.

Spring-flowering plant in good or moist lands, Pennsylvania to Georgia and Alabama, westward to Arkansas, Nebraska and Minnesota; a characteristic native plant in many guises, the leafage often making it look broader than high, at other times narrow and rather slender. It is often known as Stagger-weed, from its poisonous effect on browsing cattle.

triste. Nearly simple, to 3 feet, pubescent: leaves 3–5-parted and the parts again sharply cut, ciliate, nerves hairy, otherwise glabrous: inflorescence a simple open raceme, the pedicels long and erect or bent at top; flowers about a dozen, brown to brown-purple, grayish-pubescent, large, to about 1½ inches long, the ovate sepals scarcely equalled by the spur; petals dark violet, the upper ones hairy at apex, lower bearded: follicles 3, densely pubescent, nearly ¾ inch long; seeds squamate in ridges.—*D. triste*, Fischer 1824.

Mountains in Siberia. An oddity because of its color; little planted.

trolliifolium. Coarse glabrous plant to 6 feet tall, leafy: leaves rather thin, to 5 inches across, orbicular in general outline, cleft into 5–7-cuneate parts that are again cut or lobed or sometimes with blunt teeth but those on upper part of stem with acute teeth: inflorescence a loose raceme or perhaps dense in its upper part, to 2 feet long, the divaricate hairy or glabrous pedicels 2 inches or less long except the lower ones which may be 4 or 5 inches long; flowers deep blue, about ¾ inch long; spur very slender, much exceeding the sepals: follicles 3, glabrous, to 1 inch long.—*D. trolliifolium*, Asa Gray 1872.

Northern California, Oregon; one of the cow poisons.

truncatum: garden plant of the *elatum* kind.

uliginosum. Small plant with a short tap-root, glabrous or lightly pubescent, usually less than 2 feet tall: leaves mostly basal and 1–3 inches in breadth or length, rather prominently stalked, glabrous; blades of early leaves not deeply divided but cut or toothed less than half way down, of the later ones cut to base: inflorescence a terminal moderately close raceme, pedicels finely pubescent and the lower ones not much elongated; flowers blue, sometimes pink, about 1 inch long, standing crosswise or nearly so, the straight or slightly curved spur equalling or exceeding the broad obtuse sepals; petals notched, color of sepals, ciliate: follicles 3, puberulent, to ½ inch long; seeds densely squamate.—*D. uliginosum*, Curran 1885.

Northern central California, by streams and on moist banks.

urceolatum. Plate 13. Stem to 5 feet, erect, terete, hirsute below but glabrous toward the top: leaves petiolate, deeply 5-palmate, deep green and veined and glabrescent on upper face, pale green and ribbed and thin-hairy underneath, lobes long-lanceolate, acuminate, somewhat 3-lobed or otherwise cut, petiole hairy, parts ascending into an urceolate (urn-shaped) or broadly bell-shaped form: inflorescence a terminal open simple somewhat hirsute raceme to 1 foot long, pedicels hairy, bracts subtending pedicels simple or 2–3-lobed; flowers blue suffused with dull red, standing crosswise; sepals equal and acute, hairy on back and ciliate on margins; spur somewhat curved, about equalling the sepals, rugose; petals darker colored, narrow, plane, upper ones erect: follicles 3, lightly hairy; seeds angled, blackish at maturity, not squamate.—*D. urceolatum*, Jacquin 1781.

Nativity not recorded; see discussion under Garland larkspur, beginning page 52.

variegatum. ROYAL LARKSPUR. Showy species to 18 inches tall, simple or branched in the inflorescence, leaves mostly basal, stem hairy-pubescent, rising from thickened roots or a cluster of tubers: leaves small, to 2½ inches across, cordate-orbicular to reniform in outline, somewhat hairy, parted nearly to base into flat oblong pronged segments, ultimate lobes obtuse on lower leaves and acute on the upper simple ones: inflorescence of one rather open short central and perhaps two or more lateral few-flowered racemes, the erect pedicels pubescent; flowers royal purple but varying to light lavender, 1–1½ inches across, standing nearly or quite crosswise; spur rather stout, straight or perhaps curved at tip, about equalling the very broad obtuse sepals; upper petals whitish, lower ones usually colored like sepals: follicles 3, about 3 inches long more or less, pubescent; seeds white-winged, not squamate.—*D. variegatum*, Torrey & Gray 1838.

Grassy hills of Coast ranges, middle California. I have seen *D. grandiflorum* cultivated under the name *variegatum*.

vestitum. Hirsute, to about 3 feet tall, the stem simple, the petioles with long expanded somewhat sheathing base: leaves long-hairy on both surfaces, cordate, the blade divided to middle into 5–7 cuneate coarsely crenate-serrate lobes: inflorescence a straight long many-flowered raceme, bearing hairy bracts; flowers pale blue, densely hairy; sepals broad-lanceolate and acute, nearly equalled by the somewhat curved spur; petals dark blue, the upper ones densely hairy, the lower ones bifid and bearded: follicles 3, hairy, nearly ½ inch long; seeds narrowly winged, not squamate.—*D. vestitum*, Wallich 1831.

Himalayas, to 12,000 feet.

villosum. Tall, leafy: leaves glabrous except on margins and nerves, 3–7-parted and the parts again deeply cut or pinnatifid, the ultimate lobes lanceolate and acute, upper leaves much less divided: inflorescence an open raceme, the lower bracts 3-parted; flowers blue, pubescent to nearly glabrous, spur equalling the sepals; petals brownish-purple, the lower ones yellow-bearded: follicles 3 or 4, lightly pubescent to hairy; seeds with narrow wings, smooth.—*D. villosum*, Steven 1818.

Europe and Asia: Russia, Turkestan, Siberia. A form with loose inflorescence is *D. laxiflorum*, DeCandolle 1818, apparently not in cultivation, the plant grown under that name being a garden form of Garland or Candle larkspur. *D. villosum* is little known in cultivation.

vimineum. Apparently a form of *D. virescens* without glandular pubescence and more bluish flowers. The name starts with Don in 1838, applied to a plant in cultivation in England, the seeds taken "most probably either in Louisiana or Texas" by Thomas Drummond, known as a collector in North America. In present treatment of Delphinium the name may be applied to plants native in Texas.

virescens. Small and slender or stout depending on circumstances, 1–3 feet tall, mostly leafy, upper part of stem glandular-pubescent and lower part only partly so, from a stout more or less clustered thickened root: leaves thinly pubescent, 2–4 inches across, deeply divided into many long and narrow acute segments: inflorescence an open raceme that is short or elongated, the pubescent pedicels mostly very short and bracted at top; flowers white or faintly bluish-white, somewhat pubescent, mostly declined on the axis, 1–1 ¼ inches long; spur somewhat ascending or upstanding, straight or curved, about as long as the blunt rather broad sepals or sometimes exceeding them; petals usually yellowish tinted or splashed: follicles 3, ½–¾ inch long, pubescent.—*D. virescens*, Nuttall 1818; *D. albescens*, Rydberg 1899.
Manitoba to Wisconsin and Oklahoma to Texas.

var. **Penardii.** Lower part of stem glandular-pubescent, upper part plainly pubescent.—*D. virescens* var. *Penardii*, Perry 1937; *D. Penardii*, Huth 1892; collected in Colorado by E. Penard in 1891.
Nebraska and Colorado to Texas.

Wellbyi. Pilose erect perennial to about 2 feet tall, with few usually 3-flowered side branches: stem-leaves about 2 inches across, 5-parted, the segments 3–7-lobed with lobes acute: flowers blue, pubescent, about 2 inches or more across, the stalks 2 inches long more or less, in a short raceme, 2-bracted; sepals about ¾ inch long, broadly obovate, about one-half the length of the arched attenuate but scarcely acute upright spur; upper petals shorter than sepals, 2-lobed, lower ones entire and very narrow: follicles 3, pilose.—*D. Wellbyi*, Hemsley 1907.
Abyssinia; collected in 1898 by Capt. M. S. Wellby. I have not seen this species in cultivation, the plant so named being erroneous.

yunnanense. Stem erect to 3 feet: leaves 5–7-parted, the parts cuneate at the base and deeply cut-lobed: flowers deep blue; spur slender, about ¾ inch long and much exceeding the sepals; upper petals brownish and glabrous, lower ones blue and 2-lobed and lightly bearded: follicles 3, glabrous; seeds winged on the angles, granular but not squamate.—*D. yunnanense*, Franchet 1893.
Province Yunnan in western China, and eastern Tibet. The culti-

vated plant I have seen under this binomial is incorrectly named. True *yunnanense* has leaves orbicular in outline and with obtuse ultimate lobes; flowers in a long raceme.

Zalil. Nearly simple perennial to 2 feet tall, puberulent, from a thick branching woody root: leaves deeply divided into linear-acuminate rigid segments with recurved margins, base of petiole not dilated: inflorescence a loosely flowered raceme, the pubescent short pedicels erect in axil of a long linear bract; flowers primrose-yellow with gland on each broad acute sepal, about 1 inch across; spur nearly or quite straight, acute, about equalling the sepals; petals narrow and 2-lobed, much shorter than sepals and similar in color, bearded: follicles 3, glabrous, 5-ribbed and reticulate; seeds somewhat 4-angled, and squamate or lamellate crosswise.—*D. Zalil*, Aitchison & Hemsley 1888.

Persia, where it is known as Zalil, the flowers used in dyeing. At the proper season the hillocks of its region are reported to be resplendent with its color.

The Rocket Larkspur, a well known flower-garden annual.

Index

to the items excepting those in alphabetic
sequence in the Enumeration